Fr

M

7

HOMEWORK ANSWERS

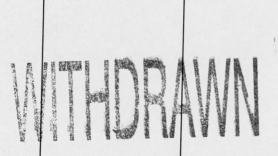

Peter Johnson	Wellfield High School, Leyland, Lancashire
Penny Jones	Mathematics Consultant, Birmingham
Jayne Kranat	Langley Park School for Girls, Bromley
Ian Molyneux	St. Bedes RC High School, Ormskirk
Peter Mullarkey	School Improvement Officer, Manchester
Nina Patel	Ifield Community College, West Sussex

OXFORD
UNIVERSITY PRESS

OXFORD

UNIVERSITY PRESS

Great Clarendon Street, Oxford OX2 6DP

Oxford University Press is a department of the University of Oxford.
It furthers the University's objective of excellence in research, scholarship,
and education by publishing worldwide in

Oxford   New York

Auckland   Cape Town   Dar es Salaam   Hong Kong   Karachi
Kuala Lumpur   Madrid   Melbourne   Mexico City   Nairobi
New Delhi   Shanghai   Taipei   Toronto

With offices in

Argentina   Austria   Brazil   Chile   Czech Republic   France   Greece
Guatemala   Hungary   Italy   Japan   Poland   Portugal   Singapore
South Korea   Switzerland   Thailand   Turkey   Ukraine   Vietnam

Oxford is a registered trade mark of Oxford University Press
in the UK and in certain other countries

British Library Cataloguing in Publication Data

Data available

ISBN-13: 978-0-19-974930-8
ISBN-10: 0-19-914930-5

3 5 7 9 10 8 6 4 2

Typeset by Techset Ltd., Gateshead, Tyne and Wear
and Bridge Creative Services, Oxon

Printed in Great Britain

Contents

A1   Sequences and functions

A1.1HW   Introducing sequences

1   **a**   7, 14, 21, 28, 35   **b**   6, 5, 4, 3, 2
    c   1, 3, 9, 27, 81   **d**   1, 2, 4, 8, 16
    e   13, 15, 17, 19, 21
2   **a**   14, 17, 20   **b**   16, 21, 26
    c   14, 12, 10   **d**   8, 7, 7
    e   3, 7, 9   **f**   8, 11, 20, 23
    g   19, 17, 13, 9   **h**   8, 7, 6, 4, 3
    i   21, 28   **j**   36, 49

A1.2HW   Sequences and rules

1   **a**   5, add 5   **b**   1, add 4
    c   20, subtract 3, 8   **d**   8, 10, 18, add 2
2   **a**   8, 17, 20; start at 2 and add 3
    b   20, 15, 5; start at 20 and subtract 5
    c   25; square numbers starting from 1
    d   8, 64; start at 2 and double
    e   25; start at 100 and halve
    f   21, 24; start at 18 and add 3

A1.3HW   Sequences in diagrams

1   **i**   **a**   Start with 5 squares and add 1 square.
       b

       c   9, 10
   ii   **a**   Start with 3 triangles and add 2 triangles.
       b

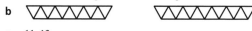

       c   11, 13
   iii   **a**   Start with 1 star and add 2 stars.
       b

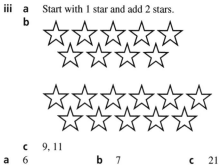

       c   9, 11
2   **a**   6   **b**   7   **c**   21

A1.4HW   Function machines

1   **a**   10
    b   42
    c   4
    d   6
2   **a**   11, 22, 33
    b   0.5, 1, 1.5
    c   9, 10, 11
    d   0, 1, 2
3   **a**   11, 13, 15
    b   3, 6, 9

A1.5HW   Finding the function

1   **a**   3, 6, 9
    b   8, 9, 10
2   **a** $+4$ **b** $\times 2$
    c $\times 4$ **d** $\times 9$
    e $+7$ **f** $+0, -0, \times 1$ or $\div 1$
3   **a** $\times 5, +4$
    b   They are the same.
4   Examples of functions are $+3$ (5, 6) and $\times 4$ (8, 12).

A1.6HW   Functions and algebra

1   **a**   There are n computers in America.
    b   There are c crayons in a pencil case.
    c   There are b bananas growing on a tree.
    d   There are s stars in the universe.
2   **a** $2j$ **b** $5y$ **c** $12g$ **d** $2.5m$
3   **a**   There are $2j$ jugs in two cupboards.
    b   There are $5y$ sweets in five bags.
    c   There are $6b$ fish in six ponds.
    d   In 12 haunted houses there are $12g$ ghosts.
    e   There are $10c$ crayons in ten pencil cases.
4   **a** $2n$ **b** $n+1$ **c** $n-3$ **d** $n-2$

A1 SAT Level 3

a   5
b   1
c   4
d   18, 23, 28
e   1st column: 35, 34, 33   3rd column: 45, 44, 43

A1 SAT Level 4

a   4
b   24
c   36
d   10

SUPPORT

N1 Number calculations

SUPPORT

N1.1HW Place value and ordering
1 7200
2 Seven point three two
3 3.09, 3.16, 3.32, 3.5, 3.9
4 a $^-7 < 2$ b $9.1 > ^-1.2$
   c $7.12 < 7.9$ d $^-7.12 > ^-7.9$

N1.2HW Negative numbers
Students are asked to design a centigrade thermometer.

N1.3HW Negative numbers
1 a Down 150 m or $^-$150m.   b Up 50 m or $^+$50m.
   c Up 250 m etc.   d Up 200 m
   e Down 50 m   f Up 100 m
   g Up 200 m   h Down 300 m
   i Up 350 m
2 $^-$125 m
3 a Higher   b $^+$50 m

N1.4HW Mental strategies
Students are asked to design a poster on mental addition and subtraction of decimals.

N1.5HW Add and subtract decimals
1 a The tens column should be $12 - 5 = 7$, not $5 - 2$.
   b The tens column should be $1 - 1 = 0$, as a ten was carried over to the units column.
   c The units column should be $16 - 9 = 7$, not $9 - 6$.

2 a The decimal points were not lined up correctly.
   b 43 was positioned in the wrong columns.
   c The decimal points were not lined up correctly.

3 a The answer in the tens column should have been $3 + 2 + 1 = 6$, not $3 + 2 = 5$ carried into the hundreds column.
   b The answer in the hundreds column should have been $8 + 1 + 1 = 10$, not $8 + 1 = 9$ carried into the hundreds column.
   c The answer in the hundredths column should be 3 with one carried over to the tenths column. Decimal point not aligned.

N1.6HW Using a calculator
1 a 775   b 632
   c 11 939   d 4577
   e 8013   f 959
2 a £27.19   b £40.33
   c $^-$£5.97   d £51.30
   e £82.72   f £14.18
3 a 10 404   b 11 784
   c 4364   d 5370.9
   e 1106   f 646
4 a 3.2
   b 0.9
   c 9

N1 SAT Level 3
a bird   b diver   c fish

N1 SAT Level 4
c 5 °C   d 11

S1 Perimeter and area

S1.1HW Perimeter and area

1 a 24 cm, 20 cm²
  b 10 cm, 6 cm²
  c 14 cm, 12 cm²
  d 18 cm, 18 cm²
2 i a 12 cm   b 8 cm²
  ii a 20 cm   b 24 cm²
  iii a 18 cm   b 20 cm²
3 20 to 24 cm²

S1.3HW Measurements and scales

1 3−4 m, 800−1000 m, 400 g, 2, m², 25 minutes past 3, 300−400 ml
2 Student's own work.

S1 SAT Level 3

a 190 ± 1

S1.2HW More perimeter and area

1 14, 10
  20, 21
  16, 16
  28, 48
  30, 56
2 a 32 cm, 44 cm²
  b 26 cm, 22 cm²
3 30 m

S1.4HW Three dimensional shapes

1

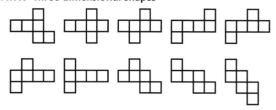

  b They all have the same perimeter of 14 units.
2 a 2 × 3 × 4
  b 52 square units

S1 SAT Level 4

a 5 cm², 12 cm   d 7 cm²   e diagonals > 1 cm

N2 Fractions, decimals and percentages

N2.1HW Understanding fractions

There are no unique solutions to this investigation.

N2.3HW Add and subtract fractions

1 $\frac{2}{12}$ 2 $\frac{4}{6}$ 3 $\frac{9}{12}$
4 $\frac{6}{10}$ 5 $\frac{5}{10}$ 6 $\frac{3}{15}$

N2.5HW Fractions of an amount

1 $\frac{1}{3}$ of 90, $\frac{1}{5}$ of 50, $\frac{1}{10}$ of 300 or similar
There are no unique solutions to this investigation.

N2 SAT Level 3

a 3   b $\frac{1}{2}$ c 15

N2.2HW Equivalent fractions

1 $\frac{8}{20}$ 2 $\frac{3}{12}$ 3 $\frac{7}{21}$
4 $\frac{9}{20}$ 5 $\frac{3000}{1000}$ 6 $\frac{15}{20}$

N2.4HW Fractions and decimals

Students are asked to design a poster showing fraction and decimal conversion.

N2.6HW Fractions, decimals and percentages

There are no unique solutions to this investigation.

N2 SAT Level 4

a

b 1, 24, 4

D1   Statistics and probability

D1.1HW Finding the average
1   a   Mode = 4, median = 5
    b   Mode = 17, median = 13
    c   Mode = 1, median = 10
2   a   3.5
    b   Yes. No-one actually read 3.5 books, but the extreme value of 55 does not distort the median.
3   Using given extract:
    a   3, 5 (two modes).
    b   Easy to read.

D1.2HW The mean
1   a   5 m
    b   16p
2   a   £6
    b   None of the students gets £6 pocket money.
3   a   8.4
    b   It isn't a whole number of sweets.
4   a   Student's own answer.
    b   60 years

D1.3HW Interpreting diagrams
1   a   4 million
    b   3 million
2   a   45–54 years
    b   65+ years
3   No, the ages are grouped so you cannot tell how many people aged 28 travelled from the UK. The age group is 25–34.
4   1   On the whole more people visit the UK than travel abroad from the UK. This may be because the UK is a very popular tourist destination. Also, the UK population is much smaller than the total population of other countries.
    2   A greater proportion of children aged 0–15 visit the UK than travel abroad from the UK. This may be because in other countries children are included in society more than in the UK, etc.

D1.4HW Introducing probability
1   a   Equally likely, same number of black and white beads
    b   Boys are more likely to win, more white beads than black
    c   Boys are certain to win, there are no black beads
2   The probability that the girls win using bag 1 is $\frac{1}{2}$
    The probability that the girls win using bag 2 is $\frac{2}{5}$
    The probability that the girls win using bag 3 is 0
    The probability that the boys win using bag 1 is $\frac{1}{2}$
    The probability that the boys win using bag 2 is $\frac{3}{5}$
    The probability that the boys win using bag 3 is 1

D1.5HW Calculating probabilities
1   $\frac{12}{20} = \frac{3}{5}$ or 0.6
2   a   18
    b   10 soft and 8 hard, 11 soft and 7 hard, 12 soft and 6 hard
3   a $\frac{12}{16} = \frac{3}{4}$ b $\frac{4}{16} = \frac{1}{4}$

D1.6HW Experimental probability
1   Blue $\frac{3}{10}$, green $\frac{1}{5}$, red $\frac{2}{5}$, yellow $\frac{1}{10}$
2   2, if $\frac{1}{10}$ is yellow then you would expect $\frac{2}{10}$ to be yellow, or $\frac{1}{10}$ of 20 is 2.

D1 SAT Level 3
a   9   b   22
c   11   d   4

D1 SAT Level 4
a   Sector for train should have an angle of 54°–66°. It should start within 2 mm of the centre.
b   Train 3, bicycle 9, car 3
c   More pupils in Sara's class.

A2 — Expressions and formulae

A2.1HW Using letter symbols

Jack has 5 boxes of staples. There is a large, unknown quantity of staples in each box.

$5x$

Jack has $5x$ staples altogether.

A newspaper has 60 pages. Jaz delivers lots of newspapers.

$60x$

Jaz has to deliver $60x$ pages of newspaper.

There are lots of feathers on a duck.

$15x$

There are $15x$ feathers on 15 ducks.

There are 4 wheels on a car. There are too many cars to count in the car park.

$4x$

In the city car park, there are $4x$ wheels altogether.

In 3 bags of sugar there are $3x$ grains.

A2.2HW Rules of algebra

1, $x - 3$, x, $x + 1$, $x + 6$, 5

A2.3HW Simplifying expressions

1	a	3	b	1	c	2
	d	2	e	2	f	1
	g	2	h	3	i	1
	j	1	k	2	l	3

2	a	12	b	$5t + 7f$	c	5
	d	$5d + 5e - 10$	e	2	f	$2t$
	g	8	h	$8a$	i	$4s + 10y + 15$
	j	$6f$	k	$4d + 5e$	l	$7y + 5r$
	m	$15x$	n	$20x + 20y$	o	$5f + 9g + 22h$

A2.4HW Substitution

1	a	12	b	20
	c	25	d	27
	e	70	f	55
	g	24	h	36

2	a	$8x$, 24	b	Cannot be simplified, 33
	c	$3w + 2x + 14y$, 51	d	$s + 9t$, 92
	e	$5x + 2y$, 31	f	$7g - f$, 37
	g	$8x + 3y$, 86	h	Cannot be simplified, 28

3   Student's own answer.

A2.5HW Using formulae

1   60 seconds = 1 minute
This formula changes minutes into seconds
Sixty times the number of minutes = the number of seconds

100 pence = £1
This formula changes pounds (£) into pence.
One hundred times the number of pounds = the number of pence

10 mm = 1 cm
This formula changes millimetres (mm) into centimetres (cm).
Ten times the number of centimetres = the number of millimetres

1000 m = 1 km
This formula changes metres (m) into kilometres (km).
One thousand times the number of metres = the number of kilometres

2	a	300 seconds
	b	300p
	c	80 mm
	d	3 minutes
	e	3000 m
	f	1.5 km
	g	17.5 cm
	h	550p

A2 SAT Level 3

a   20   b i 2 ii 1   c   4

A2 SAT Level 4

i $3a$ ii $3b + 2c$ iii $2d + 7$ iv $4e + 4f + 8$

S2   Angles and shapes

S2.1HW Time for a change
1   8.05 am, 6.15 pm, 10.50 am, 8.35 pm
2   08.05, 18.15, 10.50, 20.35
3   **a**   10.45 am
    b   7.30 pm
    c   4.15 pm
    d   7.40 am
4   **a**   20 minutes
    b   In 5 minutes. 14 : 35
5   **a**   120°   **b**   60°
    c   180°   **d**   60°

S2.2HW Angles and lines
a

 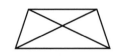

b   Square, rhombus, kite, isosceles trapezium
c   Square, rhombus, rectangle, parallelogram
d   Square, rhombus, kite, isosceles trapezium
e   No

S2.3HW Coordinates and shapes
1   **a**   (1, 3)   **b**   (0, 3)
    c   (3, 2)   **d**   (4, 0)
2   (5, 0)
    Perimeter = 8 units, Area = 3 square units
3   (4, 6), (6, 2)

S2 SAT Level 3
a   7:55   **b**   33   **c**   14:20

S2 SAT Level 4
a   90°   **b**   6   **c**   30°
d   150°   **e**   1 hour, or 60 minutes

D2   Handling data

D2.1HW Discussing statistical methods
There are no unique solutions to this investigation.

D2.2HW Data handling
2   Options are not exact. 'Very often' may mean once a week to one person and every day to another. Replace options with specific amounts.
3   Leading question. Remove words like 'fast', 'exciting', 'slow' and 'boring'.
4   People may not know of may not have an opinion. Include 'Don't know' or 'Not sure' as an option.

D2.3HW Data handling
1   Total Frequency: 10, 8, 6, 4, 2
2   Total Frequency: 6, 10, 10, 9, 11, 3, 1

D2.4HW Displaying your results
Student's own answer.

D2.5HW Interpreting your diagrams
Student's own answer.

D2 SAT Level 3
a   Missing entries: 25p, Jan, Kim, Wyn
b   £1.10
c   £20.25
d   **i** £18   **ii** £4.50

D2 SAT Level 4
a   40p is the amount most frequently spent.
b   7pm to 8pm (top to bottom): no entry, ||, |||, |||
    Total number of people: 10, 4, 3
c   More people spent 50p to 90p than any other amount.
d   **i**   Amount rises in the evening.
       ii Plausible reason

N3   Multiplication and division

N3.1HW Number and measures
1. 2500
2. 25
3. 250
4. 2.5
5. 3200
6. 32
7. 320
8. 750
9. 75
10. 7.5

N3.2HW Order of operations
1. $(8 + 4) \div 2 + 2 = 8$
   $(8 + 4) \div (2 + 2) = 3$
   $8 + 4 \div (2 + 2) = 9$
2. $3 + (6 \times 5) - 1 = 32$
   $(3 + 6) \times 5 - 1 = 44$
   $(3 + 6) \times (5 - 1) = 36$
   $3 + 6 \times (5 - 1) = 27$
3. $2 - (2 \times 2) + 2 = 0$ or $(2 - 2) \times (2 + 2) = 0$
   $(2 - 2) \times 2 + 2 = 2$
   $2 - 2 \times (2 + 2) = {}^-6$
4. $1 + (3 \div 2) + 1 = 3\frac{1}{2}$
   $(1 + 3) \div 2 + 1 = 3$
   $(1 + 3) \div (2 + 1) = 1\frac{1}{3}$
   $1 + 3 \div (2 + 1) = 2$

N3.3HW Mental methods

×	4	6	8	5
14	56	84	112	70
22	88	132	176	110
31	124	186	248	155
18	72	108	144	90
61	244	366	488	305

N3.4HW Multiplying by partitioning
Student's own answer.

N3.5HW Multiplying on paper
1. 20 and 30 have been entered in the grid as 2 and 3 respectively.
2. 30×30 is 900 not 90.
3. They have added 2 and 6 to make 8, instead of multiplying.

N3.6HW Dividing on paper
a. 32
b. 16

N3.7HW Dividing with remainders
Student's own answer.

N3.8HW Calculator methods
2. 9
3. a. 262   b. $6\frac{7}{11}$ or 6.63
   c. 120   d. 14
   e. 7.5   f. 24
   g. 411   h. 8

N3 SAT Level 3
a. ${}^-75$ b. $\div 6$

N3 SAT Level 4
a. 325, 6, 780, 1300   b. 1040

A3 | Functions and graphs

A3.1HW Factors and primes
1 a 17, 29, 11, 23, 7   **b** 7, 11, 17, 23, 29
  c 7 crossed out
2 a 12, 10, 24, 16, 18, 15, 21
  b 12 has 6 factors: 1, 2, 3, 4, 6, 12
    10 has 4 factors: 1, 2, 5, 10
    24 has 8 factors: 1, 2, 3, 4, 6, 8, 12, 24
    16 has 5 factors: 1, 2, 4, 8, 16
    18 has 6 factors: 1, 2, 3, 6, 9, 18
    15 has 4 factors: 1, 3, 5, 15
    21 has 4 factors: 1, 3, 7, 21
  c 4, 5, 6, 8

A3.3HW Squares and triangles
1 a $8^2 = 8 \times 8 = 64$ **b** **4** squared $= 4 \times 4 = 16$
  c 3 **squared** $= 3 \times 3 = 9$ **d** $6^2 = 6 \times 6 = 36$
  e $5^2 = 5 \times 5 = 25$ **f** **2** squared $= 2 \times 2 = 4$
2 a 256, 65 536, 4 294 967 296
  b 6561, 43 046 721, $1.853\ 020\ 189 \times 10^{15}$
  c 390 625, $1.525\ 878\ 906 \times 10^{11}$, $2.328\ 306\ 437 \times 10^{22}$
  d 100 000 000, 1×10^{16}, 1×10^{32}
  e 16 777 216, $2.814\ 749\ 767 \times 10^{14}$, $7.922\ 816\ 251 \times 10^{28}$
3 7 cm by 7 cm square
4 a $\sqrt{64}$ **b** $\sqrt{49}$
  c 9   **d** 4, $\sqrt{4}$
  e $3 \times 3, 3$ **f** 5, 5

A3.5HW Graphs of functions
Outputs of second machine: 3, 4, 5, 6
Coordinate pairs: (1, 3), (2, 4), (3, 5), (4, 6)

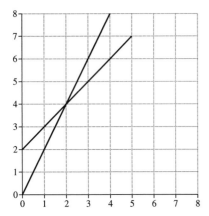

The graphs intersect at (2, 4).
Yes, by looking at the coordinate pairs.

A3 SAT Level 3
a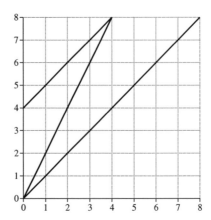
     • • • • • • • •
       • • • • • • • •
       • • • • • • • •
b Various answers
c 3, 8; 4, 6; 6, 4
d Not a whole number of seeds in each row (or equivalent explanation)

A3.2HW Patterns in numbers
8, 17, 18, 24

A3.4HW Functions and multiples
1 a Three of 2, 4, 6, …
  b Three of 3, 6, 9, …
  c Three of 4, 8, 12, …
  d Three of 5, 10, 15, …
  e Three of 6, 12, 18, …
2 a 6   **b** 4, 8, 12, 16, 20
  c 12   **d** 4, 8
  e 4
3 a Multiples of 3: 3, 6, 9, 12, 15, 18, 21, 25, 27, 30
    Multiples of 4: 4, 8, 12, 16, 20, 24, 28, 32, 36, 40
    Multiples of 6: 6, 12, 18, 24, 30, 36, 42, 48, 54, 60
  b 12
  c 6

A3.6HW Using a table of values
Function machine 1
Outputs: 2, 4, 6, 8
Coordinates: (1, 2), (2, 4), (3, 6), (4, 8)

Function machine 2
Outputs: 1, 2, 3, 4, 5, 6, 7
Coordinates: (1, 1), (2, 2), (3, 3), (4, 4), (5, 5), (6, 6), (7, 7)

Function machine 3
Outputs: 5, 6, 7, 8
Coordinates: (1, 5), (2, 6), (3, 7), (4, 8)
Agent Z has left his mark.

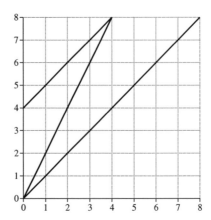

A3 SAT Level 4
a (8, 8)
b i (40, 40)   **ii** multiply tile number by 2
c The coordinates are all even numbers.
d (4, 3), (6, 5), (8, 7)
e (14, 13)
f 10

S3 Triangles and quadrilaterals

S3.1HW Measuring angles
2 Obtuse, 143°
3 Acute, 35°
4 Reflex, 240°
5 Right, 90°
6 Acute, 35°
7 Obtuse, 117°
8 Right, 90°

S3.2HW Finding angles
1 $a = 68°$
2 $b = 248°$
3 $c = 75°$
4 $d = 20°$
5 $e = 45°$
6 $f = 120°$
7 $g = 165°$
8 $h = 108°$
9 $i = 120°$
10 $j = 120°$

S3.3HW Drawing angles
a Obtuse
b 108°
c Acute
d 72°
e Acute
f 36°
g Obtuse
h 108°

Challenge
33

S3.4HW Angles in triangles
1 a $a = 90°$ **b** Right angled
2 a $b = 70°$ **b** Acute angled scalene
3 a $c = 140°$ **b** Isosceles
4 a $d = 58°$ **b** Right angled
5 a $e = 60°$ **b** Equilateral
6 a $f = 20°$ **b** Obtuse angled scalene
7 a $g = 325°$ **b** Isosceles
8 a $h = 48°$ **b** Acute angled scalene
9 a $i = 30°$ **b** Isosceles
10 a $j = 90°$ **b** Right angled isosceles

S3.5HW 2-D drawings of 3-D cubes
1 **a** 17   **b** 14
   c 13   **d** 10
   e 8   **f** 13
   g 13   **h** 14
   i 13   **j** 14
   k 19   **l** 12 or 13
   m 14
2 **a** and **d**, **b** and **c**, **e** and **k**, **i** and **m**, **h** and **g**, **f** and **j**
   l is the odd one out.

S3 SAT Level 3
a E
b D
c B

S3 SAT Level 4
a **i** 10   **ii** 16   **iii** 30
b 24

N4	Percentages, ratio and proportion

N4.1HW Fraction, decimal and percentage equivalents

1 $\frac{1}{20}, \frac{1}{10}, \frac{1}{5}, \frac{1}{4}, \frac{3}{5}, \frac{3}{4}, \frac{4}{5}$

   5%, 10%, 25%, 40%, 60%, 80%, 90%

   0.05, 0.2, 0.4, 0.6, 0.75, 0.8, 0.9

2   $\frac{1}{10}$, 10% $\frac{3}{5}$, 0.6

   $\frac{1}{5}$, 0.2 $\frac{3}{4}$, 0.75

   $\frac{1}{4}$, 25% $\frac{4}{5}$, 80%

   40%, 0.4   90%, 0.9

N4.2 Finding simple percentages

There are no unique solutions to this investigation.

N4.3HW Finding harder percentages

1 Student's own work

2 a 5

   b 15

   c $2\frac{1}{2}$

   d $17\frac{1}{2}$

   e $8\frac{3}{4}$

N4.4HW Proportion

a 1000 ml, 1500 ml

b 140p

c can: 100 ml costs **9**p

   small bottle: **1000** ml costs 85p

   10 $\times$ 100 ml costs 85p

   so 100 ml costs 85 $\div$ **10** p = **8.5**p

   large bottle: **1500** ml costs **140**p

   so **15** $\times$ 100 ml costs **140**p

   so 100 ml costs **140** $\div$ **15** p = **9.33**p

d Small bottle

N4.5HW Introducing ratio

1 a 240 g raisins   560 g margarine

       480 g dates   800 g condensed milk

       360 g sultanas   320 g plain flour

       200 g currants   2 eggs

   b You would need $\frac{1}{5}$ egg, and very small amounts of other ingredients

2 a 25 g

   b 40

   c 15 g

N4 SAT Level 3

a 240 yen

b 302 yen

c 2513 yen

d 3052 yen

N4 SAT Level 4

a 4

b 5

c 6

d 

A4   Linear equations

A4.1HW Using algebraic expressions
a $x - 4, x + 4, x - 3, 5x, x - 1$
b   Add 1 to an unknown number. $x + 1$
     Add 3 to an unknown number. $x + 3$

A4.2HW Algebraic operations
1   a   8   b   10
     c   2, 2   d $5, \div, 5$
     e $10, 4, -, 6, =$ f $-, y$
     g $3, \times$ h $8, 2, 2, \times$

A4.3HW Using brackets
1   a   10, 13, 8, 2
     b   Both the same
     c $10 \div (2 + 3) = 2$
        $8 - 2 \times 3 = 2$
     d $2 \times (3 + 4) = 14$
        $5 + 2 \times 4 = 13$
        $10 \div 2 + 3 = 8$
        $(8 - 2) \times 3 = 18$

A4.4HW Solving equations
1   a   7   b   4
     c   1   d   2
     e   12   f   8
     g   2   h   1
2   a $x = 4$ b $x = 5$
     c $x = 8$ d $x = 10$
     e $x = 2$ f $x = 4$
     g $x = 10$ h $x = 12$

A4 SAT Level 3
a   i   312   ii   22   iii   12
b   For example, 24×11 or 22×12

A4 SAT Level 4
a   50   b   16   c   10   d   10
e   27   f   7   g   100   h   10

S4   Transformations

S4.1HW Reflection symmetry
1
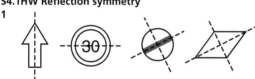
   a   1 line of symmetry   b   1 line of symmetry
   c   2 lines of symmetry   d   2 lines of symmetry

2
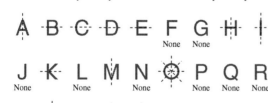

A: 1, B: 1, C: 1, D: 1, E: 1, F: 0, G: 0, H: 2, I: 2, J: 0, K: 1, L: 0,
M: 1, N: 0, O: 2, P: 0, Q: 0, R: 0, S: 0, T: 1, U: 1, V: 1, W: 1, X: 2,
Y: 1, Z: 0.

3
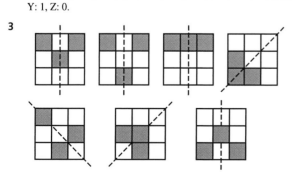

Seven 3×3 grids with three squares shaded that have one line of
symmetry

S4.2HW Reflecting shapes
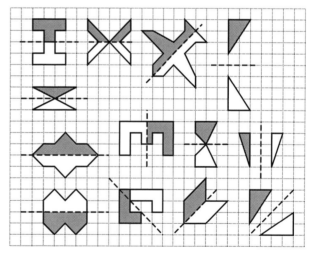

S4.3HW Reflecting in all four quadrants

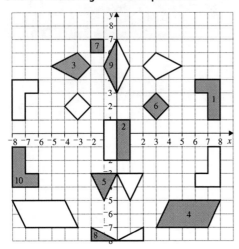

1 a Hexagon
  b (⁻8, 1), (⁻8, 4), (⁻6,4), (⁻6, 3), (⁻7, 3), (⁻7, 1), (⁻8, 1)
2 a Rectangle
  b (0, 1), (⁻1, 1), (⁻1, ⁻2), (0, ⁻2), (0, 1)
3 a Kite
  b (2, 5), (3, 6), (5, 5), (3, 4), (2, 5)
4 a Parallelogram
  b (⁻8, ⁻4), (⁻7, ⁻6), (⁻3, ⁻6), (⁻4, ⁻4), (⁻8, ⁻4)
5 a Isosceles triangle
  b (0, ⁻3), (1, ⁻5), (2, ⁻3), (0, ⁻3)
6 a Square
  b (⁻3, 1), (⁻4, 2), (⁻3, 3), (⁻2, 2), (⁻3, 1)
7 a Square
  b (1, 7), (2, 7), (2, 6), (1, 6) (1, 7)
8 a Right-angled triangle
  b (0, ⁻7), (2, ⁻7), (2, ⁻6), (0, ⁻7)
9 a Isosceles triangle
  b (0, 3), (1, 5), (0, 7), (0, 3)
10 a Hexagon
  b (7, 0), (8, 0), (8, ⁻3), (6, ⁻3), (6, ⁻2), (7, ⁻2), (7, 0)

S4.4HW Translating shapes

1

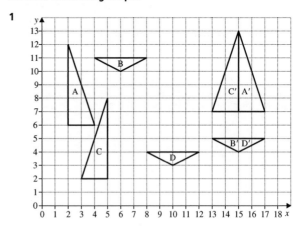

2 a 1   b 5   c 11

S4.5HW Rotation

1 b 180°   c 270°   d 360°
  e 30°   f 90°   g 240°
  h 0°   i 330°   j 45°

2

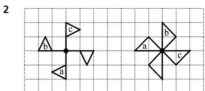

S4.6HW Transformations

1 A Translation   B Reflection   C Reflection
  D Reflection   E Rotation

2

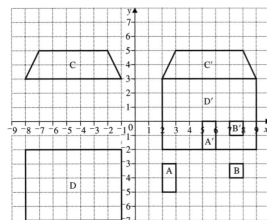

3

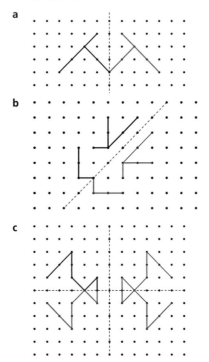

S4 SAT Level 3

a

b

c

S4 SAT Level 4

a Correct statements: quadrilateral, kite   b (5, 7)
c (7, 5)   d (7, 1)

N5 More number calculations

N5.1HW Rounding
1 **a** and **e** are rounded. **c** is shown with two decimal places, implying 2 d.p. of accuracy.

2 **a** 20
   b 70
   c 90
   d 130
   e 10
   f 120
   g 57 140

3 D

N5.2HW Factors, multiples and primes
The prime numbers are 2, 3, 5, 7, 11, 13, 17, 19, 23, 29, 31, 37, 41, 43, 47, 53, 59, 61, 67, 71, 73, 79, 83, 89 and 97.

N5.3HW Multiplying and dividing mentally
1 40
2 528
3 405
4 1400
5 23
6 636
7 22
8 525
9 71
10 510

N5.4HW Standard written calculations
a Technician
b Cook £183.75, Cleaner £195.30, Technician £176.96
c Cleaner

N5.5HW Standard written division
1 Student's own work

2 **Challenge**

230 and 10	297 and 11
378 and 14	403 and 13
465 and 15	527 and 17
779 and 19	464 and 16
666 and 18	348 and 12

N5.6HW Using equivalent fractions
FRACTIONS ARE EASY WHEN YOU GET THE HANG OF THEM

N5.7HW Converting fractions, decimals and percentages
1 **a** 0.125, 12.5%
   b 0.3, 30%
   c 0.8, 80%
   d 0.6, 66%
2 **a** $\frac{9}{20}$, 0.45
   b $\frac{7}{25}$, 0.28
   c $\frac{1}{8}$, 0.125
   d $1\frac{1}{10}$, 1.1

N5.8HW Calculating parts of quantities
There are no unique solutions to this investigation.

N5 SAT Level 3
a £6.60
b **i** £89.60
   ii 5

N1 SAT Level 4
a 58
b £24 360
c £8.12

D3 Analysing statistics

D3.1HW Planning data collection

1 Length of TV Programmes on BBC1
Weather forecast for Malaga in July
Results of 100 m men's final at the last Olympics
2 TV Listings
Met office or Internet
IOC or Internet
3 Student's own answer

D3.2HW Constructing statistical diagrams

Aberdeen has fewer passengers in 2000.

Stansted had the largest increase. (Heathrow had the same number of extra passengers, but the percentage increase was less.)

1 Bar chart heights:
Heathrow 62, Gatwick 30, Manchester 17, Stansted 9, Birmingham 7

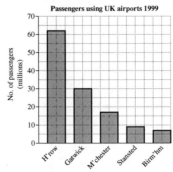

2 Bar chart heights:
Heathrow 65, Gatwick 32, Manchester 19, Stansted 12, Birmingham 8

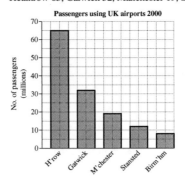

D3.3HW Comparing data using diagrams

1 a Gatwick
b The graph only shows that Gatwick is the busiest of the three airports shown. For example, Heathrow is not included.
c All three airports are becoming increasingly busy, but Stansted has the greatest increase. If the trend continues, Stansted will soon be as busy as Manchester and may eventually be as busy as Gatwick.
2 There are more male employees than female.
There are more male full-time employees than female full-time employees.
There are fewer male part-time employees than female part-time employees.
The proportion of male employees that are part-time is much smaller than the proportion of females that are part-time.
Nearly half of female employees work part-time.
Nearly all male employees work full-time.

D3.4HW Describing data using statistics

1 Frequency: 1, 9, 15, 10, 4, 13, 3, 3
2 Mean = 4.26, Median = 4, Mode = 3
The median is most suitable as the mode is too low, and the mean is not a whole number of letters.

D3.5HW Communicating results

Sport/Activity: Walking, Swimming, Cycling, Snooker/pool/billiards

Percentage of males: 49, 13, 15, 19

Percentage of females: 41, 8, 16, 4

Activity	Percentage of males	Percentage of females
Walking	49	41
Swimming	13	16
Cycling	15	8
Snooker/pool/billiards	19	4

D3 SAT Level 4

a Tally chart (with frequencies): 4(5), 5(6), 6(5), 7(8), 8(3), 9(2)
b 7 c Valid explanation.

D3 SAT Level 3

a i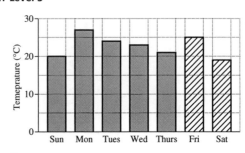

ii 27°C
b Lyn→A Chris→E Mel→C Sue→D

| D4 | **Probability experiments** |

D4.1HW Theoretical probability

1 a February, March, May, June, July, October, December
   b $\frac{1}{5}$
   c 0

2 a Monday, Wednesday, Friday, Saturday, Sunday
   b $\frac{3}{10}$
   c 0

3 a 1957, 1959, 1967, 1978, 1979, 1981, 1985, 1989, 1994
   b $\frac{1}{10}$
   c $\frac{3}{10}$
   d $\frac{1}{2}$

D4.2HW Experimental probability

Spinner 1
0.23, 0.32, 0.16, 0.29

Spinner 2
0.224, 0.164, 0.152, 0.268, 0.192

Spinner 3
0.186, 0.148, 0.132, 0.196, 0.182, 0.156

D4.3HW Comparing experiment with theory
There are no unique solutions to this investigation.

D4 SAT Level 3

a Circle, square, triangle
b Square
c More circles than squares
d 1 extra square, 2 extra circles

D4 SAT Level 4

a More gold than silver
b 3
c 5, 6, 7, or 8

A5   Equations and graphs

A5.1HW Solving equations

1
  b $x = 13$ **c** $x = 8$
  d $x = 4$ **e** $x = 9$
  f $x = 7$ **g** $x = 4$
  h $x = 5$ **i** $x = 2$
  j $x = 6$ **k** $x = 12$
  l $x = 32$

2
  a $3x = 24, x = 8$ **b** $4x = 20, x = 5$
  c $\frac{x}{2} = 6, x = 12$ **d** $\frac{x}{2} = 8, x = 24$
  e $x - 3 = 11, x = 14$ **f** $x + 5 = 17, x = 12$

3 $3x + 4 = 10, x = 2$

A5.2HW Using formulae

1
  a   Area = length multiplied by width
  b   **A**   Area = 4
        B   Length = 5, Area = 10
        C   Length = 6, Width = 5
        D   Length = 2, Width = 0.5, Area = 1
        E   Width = 1, Area = 8
        F   Length = 10, Area = 30
  c   **C** and **F**

2 $w = 3$ cm, $l = 6$ cm; $w = 4$ cm, $l = 12$ cm

A5.3HW Formulae using letters

1   Perimeter = double the length plus double the width = $2l + 2w$

2
  b   24 cm
  c   10 cm
  d   7 cm

A5.4HW Generating sequences

1
  a

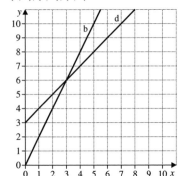

  b   Number of matchsticks: 4, 10, 16, 22, 28, 34, 40, 46
        Extra matchsticks added: −, +6, +6, +6, +6, +6, +6, +6
  c   4, 10, 16, 22, 28, 34, 40, 46, 52, 58
  d   4, add 6
  e   Next pattern = current pattern + 6

A5.5HW Spot the function

1 $4, 5, y = x + 3$

2 $\times 3, y = 3x$

3 $3, 2, y = x - 1$

4 $2, 3, y = x + 2$

5 $\div 2, y = \frac{x}{2}$

6   Two possible answers:
    $+2, 4, y = x + 2$
    $\times 3, 6, y = 3x$

7 $5, y = 2x + 1$

8   See question **6**

A5.6HW Axes in a single quadrant

a   (1, 2), (2, 4), (3, 6)

b

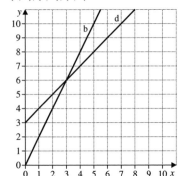

c $y = 2x$ **d**   See graph
e $y = x + 3$ **f**   (3, 6)

A5.7HW Graphs of formulae

1 y: 10, 20, 30, 40, 50, 60, 70, 80

2   (1, 10), (2, 20), (4, 40), (5, 50), (6, 60), (7, 70)

3   Points (2, 20), (4, 40), (5, 50), (6, 60), (7, 70) plotted

4
  a   30 mm   **b**   65 mm
  c   25 mm   **d**   32 mm
  e   84 mm   **f**   3.2 cm
  g   7.5 cm   **h**   9 cm

A5.8HW All four quadrants

a   Output (y): 0, 1, 2, 3
    Coordinates: (3, 0), (4, 1), (5, 2), (6, 3)

b   Points (3, 0), (4, 1), (5, 2), (6, 3) plotted

c   Point (3, 6) plotted

d   Output (y): ⁻6, ⁻5, ⁻4, ⁻3, ⁻2, ⁻1, 0, 1, 2, 3

e   Other coordinates on the line: (⁻2, ⁻5), (⁻1, ⁻4), (0, ⁻3), (1, ⁻2), (2, ⁻1)

A5 SAT Level 3

a   50   **b**   80, 100, 120
c   ⁻10, 0, 10   **d**   ⁻3, 13
e   **i**   7.9, 8, 8.1   **ii**   0.1

A5 SAT Level 4

a   (4, 2), (6, 2), (8, 2), (10, 2), (12, 2)

b x-coordinate goes up in 2s, y-coordinate is always 2

c   17 is not even.

d   (3, 3), (6, 3)

S5   Polygons

S5.1HW More angle facts

1	$a = 56°$	**7**	$g = 60°$
2	$b = 112°$	**8**	$h = 45°$
3	$c = 30°$	**9**	$i = 72°$
4	$d = 120°$	**10**	$j = 60°$
5	$e = 220°$	**11**	$k = 50°$
6	$f = 120°$	**12**	$l = 75°$

S5.2HW Constructing triangles

1   Student's own work.
2   **a**   13 cm
     b   5 cm
     c   10 cm
3   Student's own work.
4   **a**   Equilateral triangle, 60°, 60°
     b   Isosceles triangle, 70°, 70°
     c   Isosceles triangle, 80°
5   Student's own work.

S5.3HW Construction squares

1   **a**   no   **b**   no   **c**   yes

2

S5.4HW Reflection symmetry

1   Square, 4
2   Rectangle, 2
3   Kite, 1
4   Rhombus, 2
5   Parallelogram, 0
6   Isosceles trapezium, 1
7   Trapezium, 0
8   Equilateral triangle, 3

S5.5HW Rotational symmetry

1	5
2	4
3	4
4	6
5	4
6	2
7	2
8	4
9	4
10	2

S5.6HW Tessellating shapes

a

A   E

B 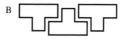   F

C 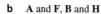   G   does not

D   H

b   **A** and **F**, **B** and **H**

S5 SAT Level 3

a   A line through the other two vertices
b   A line through a vertex and a side
c   A line through opposite sides
d   Lines through opposite vertices
e   Lines through opposite midpoints

S5 SAT Level 4

a   2   **b**   3   **c**   4   **d**   3

SUPPORT

A1   Sequences and functions

A1.1HW Introducing sequences

1   **a**   5, add 5
     b   1, add 4
     c   20, subtract 3, 8
     d   8, 10, 18, add 2

2   **a**   8, 17, 20; start at 2 and add 3
     b   20, 15, 5; start at 20 and subtract 5
     c   25; square numbers starting from 1
     d   8, 64; start at 2 and double
     e   25; start at 100 and halve
     f   21, 24; start at 18 and add 3

A1.2HW Sequences and rules

1   **a**   8, 12, 16   **b**   14, 17, 20
     c   1, 3, 7, 9   **d**   8, 11, 20, 23
     e   16, 22   **f**   16, 32
     g   36, 49   **h**   21, 28

2   A: 8, 14, 35
     B: 15, 19, 35
     C: 19, 14, 4
     D: 21
     14, 19 and 35 appear in more than one sequence.

3   Examples are:
     2, 4, 6, 8, 10; start at 2 and add 2
     2, 4, 8, 16, 32; start at 2 and double
     2, 4, 7, 11, 16; start at 2 and add 2, then increase difference by
     1 each time

4   13, 17, 21, 25, 29; start at 13 and add 4
     5, 11, 17, 23, 29; start at 5 and add 6

A1.3HW Sequences in diagrams

a   1B: 8, 14, 20, 26, 32, 38, 44, 50
     2C: 5, 8, 11, 14, 17, 20, 23, 26
     3A: 4, 7, 10, 13, 16, 19, 22, 25
b   A: add 3, B: add 6, C: add 3
c   A: 28, B: 56, C: 27
d   A: 3 multiplied by 14 then add 4
     B: 6 multiplied by 14 then add 8
     C: 3 multiplied by 14 then add 5

A1.4HW Function machines

1   14
2   45
3   19
4   48
5   45
6   103
7   3
8   3
9   7
10   5
11   9
12   11

A1.5HW Finding the function

1   **a**   ×2, ×5
     b   +7, ×2
     c   −4, ×5
     d   ×2, −4
     e   +7, −4

2   For example:
     $4 \div 2 - 1 = 1$ $4 + 1 - 3 = 2$
     $4 \div 2 + 1 = 3$ $4 \div 1 \times 1 = 4$
     $4 \div 2 + 3 = 5$ $4 + 4 - 2 = 6$
     $4 \times 2 - 1 = 7$ $4 \times 3 - 4 = 8$
     $4 \times 2 + 1 = 9$ $4 \times 3 - 2 = 10$

A1.6HW Functions and algebra

1 $5n$

2 $n + 4$

3 $n - 5$

4 $\dfrac{n}{2}$

5 $3n + 1$

6 $\dfrac{n}{4} - 2$

7 $\dfrac{n}{4} + 6$

8 $n^2 + 6$

9 $\dfrac{n}{2} + 2$

10 $^-2n - 5$

11   **a**   +7   **b**   ×2   **c**   ÷2   **d**   ×4, +1

A1 SAT Level 4

a   4
b   24
c   36
d   10

A1 SAT Level 5

a   19
b $M = 2T + 1$
c   5
d   17

CORE

N1   Number calculations

N1.1HW Place value and ordering

1   **a**   I, II, III, IV, V, VI, VII, VIII, IX, X
    b   Student's own answer.
    c   V (5), XX (20), XL (40), L (50), LV (55), LXXI (71), C (100)

2   There are no unique solutions to this investigation.

N1.3HW Negative numbers

1 $18 + 41 + {}^-9 + 21 = 71$
2 ${}^-17 + {}^-24 + {}^-13 + 11 = {}^-43$

N1.5HW Add and subtract decimals

4   For example:
    0.8,   6.3,   6.3,   0.8
    0,   5.5,   0,   5.5
    5.5,   5.5,   5.5,   5.5
    0,   0,   0,   0

N1 SAT Level 4

a $<$
b $=$
c $>$
d $<$
e $>$
f $>$

N1.2HW Negative numbers

1   **a**   Down 150 m, or -150.
    b   Up 50 m, or $+50$ etc.
    c   Up 250 m
    d   Up 200 m
    e   Down 50 m
    f   Up 100 m
    g   Up 200 m
    h   Down 300 m
    i   Up 350 m

2 -125 m

3   **a**   Higher
    b $+50$ m

N1.4HW Mental strategies

Students are asked to design a poster on mental addition and subtraction of decimals.

N1.6HW Using a calculator

1   **a**   4.2
    b   0.9
    c   1.8
    d   3.95

2   **a**   Four and a half hours
    b $1°15'$ or 1.25

3   **a**   £397.92
    b   Yes, £400 is greater than £397.92

4   **a**   11.111; estimate: $7.5 + 3.5 = 11$
    b $^-5.47$; estimate: $16 - (3 + 4 + 8 + 6) = -5$
    c   39.05; estimate: $24 - {}^-15 = 39$
    d   0.23; estimate: $\dfrac{(9 - 6)}{(9 + 6)} = \dfrac{3}{15} = 0.2$
    e   38.85; estimate: $30 - (10 - 19) = 39$

N1 SAT Level 5

a   7
b $^-8$

S1 — Perimeter and area

S1.1HW Perimeter and area
1 a 180 m², 54 m
   b 1200 cm², 160 cm
   c 170 m², 60 m
2 2 cm
3 a 8 cm², 12 cm
   b 800 mm², 120 mm
   Part **b** is 100 times part **a**, therefore there are 100 mm² in 1 cm².
4 Area of outer rectangle ≈ 4 cm × 7 cm = 28 cm²
   Area of inner rectangle ≈ 2 cm × 4 cm = 8 cm²
   Area of shape ≈ average of areas = (28 + 8) ÷ 2 = 18 cm²

S1.2HW More perimeter and area
1 20 cm
2 4 mm
3 63 in², 104 ft²
4 28 m², 32 m
5 30 tiles
6 150 tiles

S1.3HW Measurements and scales
There are no unique solutions to this investigation.

S1.4HW Three dimensional shapes
a 6 faces, 12 edges, 8 vertices, 24 cm²
b 5 faces, 9 edges, 6 vertices, 31.3 cm²
c 6 faces, 12 edges, 8 vertices, 76.3 cm²

S1 SAT Level 4
a 5 cm², 12 cm   d 7 cm   e diagonals > 1 cm

S1 SAT Level 5
a i, iii and iv   b 40

CORE

N2 — Fractions, decimals and percentages

N2.1HW Understanding fractions
There are many solutions to this investigation.

N2.2HW Equivalent fractions
Students are asked to design a poster to show equivalent fractions.

N2.3HW Add and subtract fractions
1 $\frac{154}{40} + 6\frac{3}{20} = 10$
2 $\frac{15}{4} + \frac{25}{4} = 10$
3 No, the vehicles are $40\frac{3}{10}$ m long, but there is only 30 m of space.

N2.4HW Fractions and decimals
1 If two tables have the same amount of chocolate, each person sits at the lowest numbered table.
   Person 1 sits at table 3   Person 2 sits at table 2
   Person 3 sits at table 3   Person 4 sits at table 1
   Person 5 sits at table 2   Person 6 sits at table 3
   Person 7 sits at table 1   Person 8 sits at table 2
   Person 9 sits at table 3   Person 10 sits at table 1
2 Person 11 sits at table 2   Person 12 sits at table 3
   Person 13 sits at table 1   Person 14 sits at table 2
   Person 15 sits at table 3   Person 16 sits at table 1

N2.5HW Fractions of an amount
1 Eldest son gets 9 rabbits, second son gets 6 rabbits, youngest gets 2.
2 The oldest. Before Veggie, the shares were $8\frac{1}{2}$, $5\frac{2}{3}$, $1\frac{8}{9}$. After Veggie is returned, each son will have the original number of rabbits correct to the nearest whole number. The oldest son also has the most rabbits.

N2.6HW Fractions, decimals and percentages
There are no unique solutions to this investigation.

N2 SAT Level 4
a i about $\frac{3}{4}$ ii about $\frac{1}{3}$
b i between 15% – 35%   ii 30% – 50%
c Position between 3.8 cm and 6.2 cm up the rope

N2 SAT Level 5
a i $\frac{3}{10}$ ii 30%
b i 4 triangles shaded   ii 40%

D1 Statistics and probability

D1.1HW Finding the average

1 a Median = 2°C, mode = 3°C, range = 6°C
Night temperatures, weather forecaster.

b Median = 11 mm, mode = 10 mm and 11 mm, range = 7 mm
Checking lengths, quality controller in a factory.

c Median = 3 g, mode = 2.5 g, range = 1.2 g
Weighing small quantities of chemicals, scientific researcher.

2 a Median = 6, mode = 5 and 7
The median is the best average to use, as there are two modes.

b Median = 107 cm, mode = 125 cm
The median is the best average to use, as the mode is too high.

c Median = 26p, mode = 25p
The mode is the best average to use, as it is the most common price and there is only a small range.

d Median = 45 mins, mode = 30 mins and 1 hour
The median is the best average to use, as there are two modes.

3 March: median = 32p, mode = 30p and 35p
April: median = 30p, no mode

D1.2HW The mean

1 a 5.1
b 12.6
c 3.1
d 19.9

2 Batsman B should be chosen as he has the highest mean score.
$$\frac{(102 + 108 + 116)}{3} = 108 \text{ (approx.)}$$

3 a 20 goals
b 40 m
c 4

D1.3HW Interpreting diagrams

1 a 18 years
b 16 years

2 a 7.5%
b 1.5% of 20 year old females are offenders.
c 5

3 Older people are less likely to commit crime etc.

D1.4HW Introducing probability

1 a Equally likely, same number of black and white beads.
b Boys are more likely to win, more white beads than black.
c Boys are certain to win, there are no black beads.

2 A: $\frac{1}{2}$ D: $\frac{1}{2}$
B: $\frac{2}{5}$ E: $\frac{3}{5}$
C: 0   F: 1

D1.5HW Calculating probability

1 4 soft, 5 soft and 1 hard, 6 soft and 2 hard, 7 soft and 3 hard, 8 soft and 4 hard, 9 soft and 5 hard, 10 soft and 6 hard, 11 soft and 7 hard

2 a 2 hard
b 10 soft and 7 hard

3 6 soft and 8 hard, $\frac{3}{7}, \frac{4}{7}$
7 soft and 7 hard, $\frac{1}{2}, \frac{1}{2}$
8 soft and 6 hard, $\frac{4}{7}, \frac{3}{7}$
9 soft and 5 hard, $\frac{9}{14}, \frac{5}{14}$
10 soft and 4 hard, $\frac{5}{7}, \frac{2}{7}$
11 soft and 3 hard, $\frac{11}{14}, \frac{3}{14}$
12 soft and 2 hard, $\frac{6}{7}, \frac{1}{7}$
The two probabilities add up to 1.

D1.6HW Experimental probability

1 Blue $\frac{3}{10}$, green $\frac{1}{5}$, red $\frac{2}{5}$, yellow $\frac{1}{10}$

2 a 2
b 8
c 4
d 6

3 Blue 7 or 8, green 5, red 10, yellow 2 or 3
4 Repeat the experiment.

D1 SAT Level 4

a 40p is the amount most frequently spent.
b 7pm to 8pm (top to bottom): no entry, ||, |||, |||
Total number of people: 10, 4, 3
c More people spent 50p to 90p than any other amount.
d i Amount rises in the evening.
ii Plausible reason

D1 SAT Level 5

a Q, R and T
d Second and fourth statements true
c Various possible answers

A2 — Expressions and formulae

A2.1HW Using letter symbols

1 **a** $x + 10$ **b** $x + 18$
    c $x - 12$ **d** $x - 18$

2 **a** 1 square left, 1 square up
    b 1 square left, 2 squares down
    c 5 squares right, 1 square up
    d 1 square right, 2 squares down

3 **a** 35
    b 44
    c 52
    d 22
    e 16

A2.2HW Rules of algebra

1

$2x$	double x
$x + 2$	two more than x
$\dfrac{x}{2}$	half of x
$2 - x$	x less than two
$x - 2$	two less than x
x^2	x multiplied by x
$2x - 2$	two less than double x
$2x^2 - 2x$	two less than double x, all multiplied by x

2 **a** $12ab$
    b $30a$
    c $6ab$
    d $4ab$
    e $3ab$
    f $4ab$
    g $12ab$
    h $60ab$
    i $10a^2$
    j $5a^2b$

3 **a** $4y$
    b $2y$
    c $4y$
    d $5y$
    e $2y$
    f 4

A2.3HW Simplifying expressions

1 **a** $a = 63, b = 64$ **b** $r = 46, s = 66$
    c $q = 26, p = 35$

2 **a** $2x + 2$ **b** $2y + 21$
    c $2n - 1$ **d** $2m - 22$

3 **a** $2r + 4$ **b** $2t + 11$
    c $3v$

4 For example,

$n - 2$		n	
	$n + 10$		

A2.4HW Substitution

1 $\frac{1}{2}(2d + 2)$

2 $2d - 5, 3d - 10, d^2 - 10, 1 - d, 2d - 6$

3 $4 - d, 10 - 2d$ (for a six), $12 - 4d, 1 - d$

4 Largest $d^2 - 10$, smallest $12 - 4d$

5 Largest $12 - 2d$, smallest $d^2 - 10$

6 Expressions that never gave a negative move, especially $2d + 3$ and $2d$ (or other reasoned answers)

A2.5HW Using formulae

1 $n + m + p$

2 $3p$

3 $2m$

4 $n + 2m + 3p$

5 £$1.6m$

6 £$1.9p$

7 £$(1.2n + 1.6m + 1.9p)$

Challenge

A 4 ounce patty is larger, because an ounce is approximately 28 g.

A2 SAT Level 4

i $3a$
ii $3b + 2c$
iii $2d + 7$
iv $4e + 4f + 8$

A2 SAT Level 5

a $7 + 5t$
b $3b + 17$
c $4d + 3$
d $4m$

CORE

S2 Angles and shapes

S2.1HW Finding angles

1
  a Drawing of angle ABC = 70°, acute
  b Drawing of angle XYZ = 35°, acute
  c Drawing of angle P = 120°, obtuse
  d Drawing of angle Q = 90°, right angle
  e Drawing of angle MNO = 216°, reflex
  f Drawing of angle TUV = 335°, reflex

2
  a 50°
  b 90°

3
  a 45°
  b 112°
  c 23°
  d 180°, they are angles on a straight line
  e 90°, 90°
  f 360°
  g 180°, 360°

S2.2HW Angles and lines

1
  a 62°
  b 88°
  c 57°
  d 34°

2
  a $x = 30°$, $y = 150°$
  b $z = 144°$, $t = 36°$
  c $360 - (132 + 60 + 90)$, $a = 78°$
  d $360 - (60 + 98 + 97)$, $b = 105°$

3
  a 60°
  b 35°
  c 55°
  d 35°

S2.3HW Coordinates and shapes

1 ($^-3$, $^-2$), 15 square units, 16 units

2
  a (4, 2)
  b ($^-2$, $^-3$) or similar.
  c (0, 1)
  It isn't possible to make a rectangle because the points don't join at right angles.

3 ($^-4$, $^-3$), 30 square units, 22 units

4 8 square units: (0, 3) or (0, $^-1$), (8, 3), ($^-8$, $^-1$) or 4 square units: ($^-6$, 1) or ($^-2$, 1)

5 (2, 2), (2, $^-2$)or ($^-6$, 2), ($^-6$, $^-2$); 16 square units, 16 units,

6 Student's own answer.
  Diagram and coordinates of:
  a a square
  b a rectangle
  c a right-angled triangle

S2 SAT Level 4
  a 90°
  b 30°
  c 150°
  d 1 hour, or 60 minutes

S2 SAT Level 5
  a Q
  b angle within ±2°
  c **i** 38°   **ii** 135°

D2 Handling data

D2.1HW Discussing statistical methods

1 Primary data: ask Gina and her friends what they like
Secondary data: look at music charts

2 Primary data

3 Primary data, eg. questionnaire
Secondary data, eg nutritional values from books.

D2.2HW Collecting data

There are no unique solutions to this investigation.

D2.3HW Organising the data

1 0: 10
1: 17
2: 8
3: 7
4: 6
5: 2

2 1.65−1.69: 1
1.70−1.74: 5
1.75−1.79: 5
1.80−1.84: 5
1.85−1.89: 10
1.90−1.94: 4

3 £0−£19.99: 7 (or other suitable grouping.)
£20−£39.99: 1
£40−£59.99: 2
£60−£79.99: 2
£80−£99.99: 3
£100−£119.99: 0
£120−£139.99: 1

D2.4HW Displaying your results

1 0−: 0
5−: 5
10−: 8
15−: 8
20−: 1
25−: 1
30−: 1

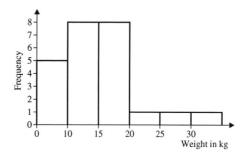

D2.5HW Interpreting your diagram

1 Video recorder and dishwasher ownership stayed steady. Mobile phone and computer ownership increased. Mobile phone ownership more than doubled.

2 Emissions have decreased overall. Industrial emissions have halved, but transport emissions have almost doubled.

D2 SAT Level 4

a Tally chart (with frequencies): 4(5), 5(6), 6(5), 7(8), 8(3), 9(2)
b 7
c Valid explanation.

D2 SAT Level 5

a Overlapping ages
c i Various answers, for example limited age group
ii Various answers, for example ease of administration

CORE

N3 Multiplication and division

N3.1HW Numbers and measures

1 2 and 200
0.2 and 20
42 and 0.42
420 and 4.2
1730 and 17.3
230 and 2.3
230 and 23 000
⁻2 and ⁻200
2400 and 24
0.03 and 3
30 and 0.3
7 and 0.07
1700 and 17

2 Student's own work.

3 $^-180 = ^-18 \times 10$ $^-20 = ^-2 \times 10$
$173 = 17.3 \times 10$ $0.7 \times 10 = 7$
$23 \times 10 = 230$ $170 = 17 \times 10$

N3.2HW Powers and operations
There are no unique solutions to this investigation.

N3.3HW Mental methods
The highest number of points is 41.

N3.4HW Multiplying on paper

1 **a** 299
   b 1122
   c 1092
   d 2336
   e 3818
   f 4788
2 **a** 5544
   b 3075
   c 7578
   d 9282
3 **a** 686
   b 1438.3
   c 1161.6
   d 22 401
   e 8013
   f 3554.7

N3.5HW Multiplying decimals

A 2747
E 632.22
L 29.43
H 329.4
N 21 834.8
G 502.46
O 774
P 644.68
C 2957.13
M 27.52
R 496.64

MELON, PEACH, GRAPE, APPLE

N3.6HW Dividing on paper

ACROSS		DOWN	
1	81	**2**	1846
3	32	**4**	242
5	86	**7**	36
6	439	**8**	911
9	24	**12**	214
10	261	**14**	33
11	612	**15**	72
13	13	**16**	11
15	71	**18**	62
17	4368	**19**	82
20	214		
21	22		

N3.7HW Dividing with remainders
There are no unique solutions to this investigation.

N3.8HW Calculator methods
There are no unique solutions to this investigation.

N3 SAT Level 4
a 134 or 143
b 431
c **i** 0 **ii** 3140
d **i** 425 or 425.0 **ii** 4250

N3 SAT Level 5
a £33.25
b 14

A3   **Functions and graphs**

A3.1HW Factors and multiples

1   2, 3, 5, 7, 11, 13, 17, 19, 23, 29, 31, 37, 41, 43, 47, 53, 59, 61, 67, 71, 73, 79, 83, 89, 97

2   5 + 47, 11 + 41, 23 + 29

3   No, 1 and 121 cannot.

A3.3HW The general term

1   **a**

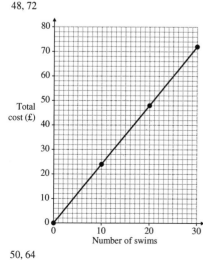

      2nd   4th

     b   No. of counters: 3, 6, 9, 12, 15, 18, 21, 24, 27, 30

     c   Add 3, 3 × table, etc.

     d   20th pattern will have 60 counters; nth pattern will have $3n$.

2

$2n + 3$ ...	First term 5, increases by 2 ...	5, 7, 9, 11, 13
$3n + 2$ ...	First term 5, increases by 3 ...	5, 8, 11, 14, 17
$5n + 2$ ...	First term 8, increases by 5 ...	8, 13, 18, 23, 28
$3n + 5$ ...	First term 8, increases by 3 ...	8, 11, 14, 17, 20
$2n + 5$ ...	First term 7, increases by 2 ...	7, 9, 11, 13, 15

3   For example, $6n - 2$. First term is 4, increases by 6, 4, 10, 16, 22, 28

A3.5HW Graphs of functions

1   **a**   ($^-$1, $^-$3), (0, 0), (1, 3), (2, 6), (3, 9)

          The y co-ordinate is three times the x co-ordinate.

     b $y = 3x$

2   **a** y: $^-$1, 1, 3, 5, 7, 9

     b   ($^-$2, $^-$1), ($^-$1, 1), (0, 3), (1, 5), (2, 7), (3, 9)

     c   Points ($^-$2, $^-$1), ($^-$1, 1), (0, 3), (1, 5), (2, 7) and (3, 9) plotted

A3 SAT Level 4

a   3 by 3 square in correct orientation   **b**   Various answers

A3 SAT Level 5

a   48, 72

b

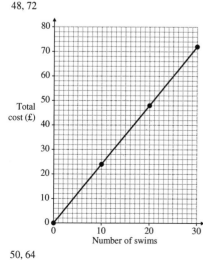

c   50, 64

A3.2HW Patterns in numbers

1

64 ← 8	3 → 9
16 ← 4	21 → 441
2.5 → 6.25	36 → 1296
81 ← 9	36 ← 6
144 ← 12	20.25 ← 4.5

2   **a**

3 × 3 = 9	13 × 13 = 169
4 × 4 = 16	14 × 14 = 196
5 × 5 = 25	15 × 15 = 225
6 × 6 = 36	16 × 16 = 256
7 × 7 = 49	17 × 17 = 289
8 × 8 = 64	18 × 18 = 324
9 × 9 = 81	19 × 19 = 361
10 × 10 = 100	20 × 20 = 400

     b   They are the same.

     c   1, 4, 9, 6, 5, 6, 9, 4, 1, 0

3   **a**   **i, ii** and **iv** (2102, 3508, 4257)

     b   **iii** and **v** are both square numbers. (2601, 3969)

A3.4HW Functions and rules

1   **a** $^-$1, 2, 5, 8

     b $y = 5x + 2$: 2, 7, 12, 17

     c $y = 2x + 3$: $^-$1, 1, 3, 5, 7

2   **a** $y = 12x + 4$

     b $y = 6x + 4$

     c   For example, Input 4, 7, 10. Rule: $y = 4x$

3   **a**   7, 4, 4

     b   2, 2, 1.5

     c $^-$3, 0, $^-$1

A3.6HW Using a table of values

1   **a**   Gradient

     b y-intercept

     c   **B** $y = x + 2$ **C** $y = x - 1$ **D** $y = x + 5$

2   Sketch of $y = 3 - x$, $y = 1 - x$, $y = 5 - x$ and $y = {}^-2 - x$

     Lines all parallel to original, crossing y-axis at 1, 5, $^-$2 respectively.

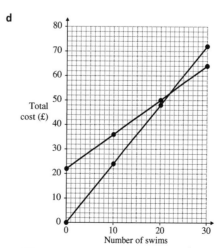

d

e   22

CORE

S3   Triangles and quadrilaterals

S3.1HW Finding angles

1   $a = 62°$
2   $b = 88°$
3   $c = 57°$
4   $d = 34°$
5   $x = 30°, y = 150°$
6   $z = 144°, t = 36°$
7   $a = 60°, b = 100°, c = 20°$
8   $l = 135°, m = 30°, n = 15°$
9   $p = 108°, q = 54°, r = 18°$
10   $a = 78°$
11   $b = 71°$
12   $c = 142°$

S3.2HW Angles in shapes

1
   a   65°   **b**   57°   **c**   30°
   d   108°   **e**   60°   **f**   80°
   g   94°   **h**   52°   **i**   100°

2
   $c + d = 180°$
   $a + b + d = 180°$
   $c + d = a + b + d$
   $c = a + b$

S3.3HW Triangles and quadrilaterals

1
   a $a = 36°, b = 36°$
   b   Angle A = 36°, angle B = 72° + 36° = 108°, angle C = 36°
   c   Student's own answer.

S3.4HW Constructing triangles

   a   Isosceles   **b**   80°
   c   Student's own answer.   **d**   Student's own answer.
   e   Student's own answer.   **f**   Angle A = 50°, angle B = 130°, angle C = 130°, angle D = 50°
   g   Parallelogram   **h**   Kite, rhombus

S3.5HW 2-D representations of 3-D shapes

1   **a**   Sketch of a triangular prism

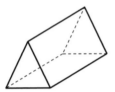

   b   5 faces, 9 edges, 6 vertices

   c   Net of a triangular prism

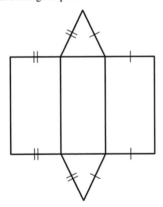

   d   Front, side and plan view of triangular prism

2   **a**   Sketch of a right-angled triangular prism

   b   Net of a right-angled triangular prism

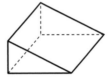
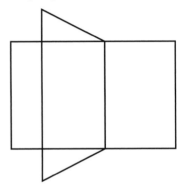

3   **a**   Sketch of a hexagonal prism

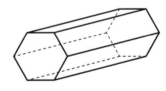

   b   8 faces, 18 edges, 12 vertices
   c   Plan view of hexagonal prism

4   **a**   Sketch of a cylinder

   b   3 faces, 2 edges, 0 vertices

   c

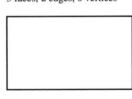
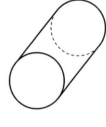
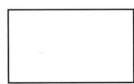

S3 SAT Level 4

Diagram completed with:

Circle radius 2 cm (±2 mm), trapezium top edge 2.5 cm (±2 mm), and triangle with angles 45°, 106°, 29° (±2°)

S3 SAT Level 5

   a   Line 10.5 cm, with angles 80° and 30°
   b   About 5.6 cm (±2 mm)
   c   About 112 m

CORE

N4 — Percentages, ratio and proportion

N4.1HW Fractions, decimals and percentages
1   Fractions: $\frac{3}{5}, \frac{5}{16}, \frac{7}{20}, \frac{17}{11}, \frac{19}{20}, \frac{5}{8}$

Decimals: 0.6, 0.313, 0.35, 1.545

Percentages: 60%, 31.3%, 35%, 154.5%, 95%, 62.5%

2   a $\frac{5}{8}$
    b $\frac{21}{16}$
    c   1.9
    d   0.3
    e $\frac{27}{17}$

3   $\frac{17}{19}$

N4.2HW Finding simple percentages
1   a   £280
    b   144 m
    c   663 apples
    d   27 120 people
    e   1032 kg
2   a   279
    b   276
    c   555
3   a   288
    b   263.2
    c   459.9
    d   1661.6
    e   470.6
4   a $0.175 \times 440 = £77$
    b   Student's own answer.

N4.3HW Comparing fractions
1   a   £183.75
    b   81 m
    c   333.61 kg
    d   85.5°
    e   £9350
    f   256.15 litres
    g   5140.8 m
2   a   18%
    b   24%
    c   25%
    d   0.32%
    e   40%
3   a   314.5 hectares
    b   £7 706 600
4   1156.68 million or 1.15668 billion
5   1 day 12 hours 57 minutes and 36 seconds

N4.4HW Proportion
1   a   336 pence or £3.36
    b   £1.14
    c   £336
    d   £251.79
2   a   504
    b   £1275
    c   52 700
3   a $\frac{2}{5}$
    b $\frac{2}{7}$
    c $\frac{3}{11}$
    d $\frac{7}{15}$
    e $\frac{3}{8}$
4   Small: £0.96 /kg.
    Medium: £0.92/kg.
    Large: £0.93/kg.
    Medium is the best value.

N4.5HW Introducing ratio
1   a   4 : 11
    b   1 : 6
    c   5 : 21
    d   2 : 11
2   a   9 : 4
    b   92 : 19
    c   3 : 1
3   a   Rufus: 45 Christabel: 75
    b   65
    c   405 (only multiple of 15 between 400 and 410)
4   Student's own answer.

N4 SAT Level 4
a   97, 90, 10, 180
b   ÷ then +

N4 SAT Level 5
a   6l red, 14l blue
b   6$\frac{1}{2}l$ yellow, 3$\frac{1}{2}l$ red

A4 Linear equations

A4.1HW Using algebraic expressions

1 a 6, 12
  b Student's own answer.

2 For example,

n	6	7

$n+6$	13

$n+19$

3 a $x + 6, 14$ $x = 10$
  b $p + 22, 41$ $p = 17$
  c $u + 25, u + 16$ $u = 21$
  d 11, 13 $v = -12$

A4.2HW Algebraic operations

1 a 6 and 5 must be in the same row/column, 3 and 8 in the other.

$$6$$
$$3 \quad 2 \quad 8$$
$$5$$

  b 3 and 9 go in the top and bottom squares (any order).
   The middle row is 7, 1, 5 (in this order).

$$9$$
$$7 \quad 1 \quad 5$$
$$3$$

  c 12 must go in the middle square, as shown.

$$4$$
$$7 \quad 12 \quad 5$$
$$8$$

  d 8 must go in the middle square.
   6 and 3 must be in the same row/column, 4 and 5 in the other.

$$3 \qquad\qquad\qquad 6$$
$$6 \quad 4 \quad 5 \quad\text{or}\quad 4 \quad 8 \quad 5$$
$$8 \qquad\qquad\qquad 3$$

2 a Middle square can be any expression that equals 3 when $x = 9$.
  b Top square can be any expression that equals 16 when $x = 5$.
   Middle square can be any expression that equals 0 when $x = 5$.
  c Top square can be any expression that equals 10 when $x = 2$.
   Middle square can be any expression that equals 3 when $x = 2$.

A4.3HW Expanding brackets

1 $5(4t - 6) = 20t - 30$ $2(10t - 12) = 20t - 24$
  $3(6t - 3) = 18t - 9$ $4(5t + 6) = 20t + 24$
  $4(5t - 7) = 20t - 28$ $9(2t + 1) = 18t + 9$
  $6(3t + 7) = 18t + 42$ $2(9t - 4) = 18t - 8$

2 $20t + 28 = 4(5t + 7)$ $8t + 12 = 4(2t + 3)$
  $18t + 24 = 6(3t + 4)$ $30t + 40 = 10(3t + 4)$
  $10t + 15 = 5(2t + 3)$ $35t + 49 = 7(5t + 7)$
  $9t + 12 = 3(3t + 4)$

3 $11\,996 \; t = 1000$
  To work out 796×5, work out $(800 - 4) \times 5$ or $(200 - 1) \times 20$.
  In algebra, this is $5(8x - 4)$ or $20(2x - 1)$ for $x = 100$.
  $796 \times 5 = 3980$

A4.4HW Solving equations

1   **b** and **j**, $x = 70$
  c and **g**, $x = 80$
  d and **h**, $x = 55$
  e and **f**, $x = 50$

2 a $a = 7$
  b $i = 12$
  c $e = 2.5$
  d $n = 20$
  e $o = 15$
  f $q = 4$
  g $t = 10$
  h $u = 5$
  equation

A4 SAT Level 4

a 4
b 5
c 6
d

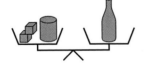

A4 SAT Level 5

a n
b $2n$
c $n + 7$
d $5n + 7$

S4 | Transformations

S4.1HW Reflection and symmetry

1
  a 4 lines of symmetry
  b 0 lines of symmetry
  c 1 line of symmetry

2 **a**   **b**   **c**

3 **a**  **b**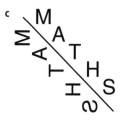

  c

S4.3HW Translating shapes

1
  a R′ with vertices at (2, 3), (⁻1, 3), (⁻1, 8), (2, 8)
  b R″ with vertices at (4, 1), (7, 1), (7, ⁻4), (4, ⁻4)
  c R‴ with vertices at (⁻1, 2),
    (2, 2), (2, ⁻3), (⁻1, ⁻3)

2
  a A′ with vertices at (⁻3, 4), (⁻3, 7), (0, 7), (0, 2)
  b A″ with vertices at (2, ⁻4),
    (5, ⁻6), (5, ⁻9), (2, ⁻9)
  c A‴ with vertices at (6, ⁻1),
    (9, ⁻1), (9, ⁻4), (6, ⁻6)

S4.2HW Reflecting shapes

a (2, 5), (6, 3), (4, 1)

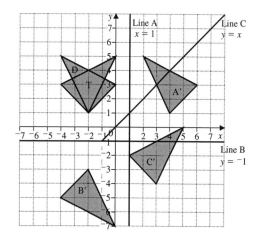

b (⁻2, ⁻3), (0, ⁻7), (⁻4, ⁻5)
c (1, ⁻2), (5, 0), (3, ⁻4)
d Mirror line is $x = ⁻2$

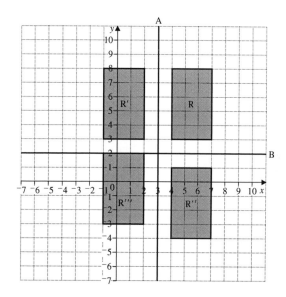

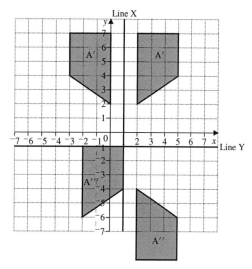

CORE

S4.4HW Rotating shapes

1 a (4, 2)
   b Rotation 90° clockwise about (2, 1)
   c Rotation 90° anticlockwise about (2, 1)
2 a Vertices at (0, 2), (0, 5), (1, 3)
   b (0, 2)
3 a Vertices at (3, ⁻1), (4, ⁻2), (1, ⁻2)
   b (1, ⁻2)
   c One unit left and three units down

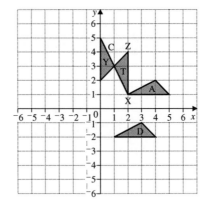

S4.5HW Symmetry

a A: 0 lines, order 2
   B: 2 lines, order 2
   C: 3 lines, order 3
   D: 0 lines, order 2
   E: 0 lines, order 3
   F: 1 line, order 1
b Student's own work.

Lines of symmetry

		0	1	2	3
Order of rotational symmetry	1		F		
	2	A, D		B	
	3	E			C

S4.6HW Transformations

a (2, 1), (5, 3), (5, 1)
b (⁻2, 1), (⁻5, 1), (⁻5, 3)
c (2, ⁻1), (5, ⁻1), (5, ⁻3)
d (1, 2), (1, 5), (5, 3)
e (1, ⁻2), (3, ⁻5), (1, ⁻5)
f Student's own work.

Line x = y

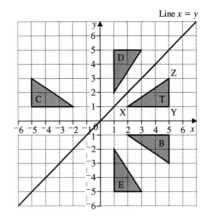

S4 SAT Level 4

a i
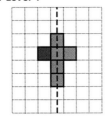

   ii
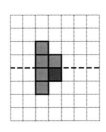

b i
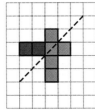

   ii

S4 SAT Level 5

Lines of symmetry

		0	1	2	3
Order of rotational symmetry	1	E	F		
	2	B		C	
	3	D			A

N5   More number calculations

N5.1HW Rounding

1   **a**   300, 350
    b   800, 820
    c   1700, 1740
    d   12 900, 12 890
    e   4000, 4000
    f   200 km, 250 km
    g   100, 110
    h   4200 g, 4200 g

2   **a**   6, 6.4
    b   3, 2.8
    c   4, 4.0
    d   7, 6.6
    e   28, 27.6
    f   24, 23.7
    g   27, 26.8
    h   13 tonnes, 13.3 tonnes

3   **a**   25   **b**   24

4   Student's own answer.

N5.2HW Factors, multiples and primes

1   **a**   1, 2, 3, 4, 6, 8, 12, 24
    b   1, 2, 4, 8, 16, 32
    c   1, 2, 5, 10, 25, 50
    d   1, 61
    e   1, 71
    f   1, 2, 3, 4, 5, 6, 8, 10, 12, 15, 20, 24, 40, 60, 120
    g   1, 2, 3, 4, 6, 8, 9, 12, 16, 18, 24, 36, 48, 72, 144
    h   1, 2, 4, 5, 10, 11, 20, 22, 44, 55, 110, 220

2   16, 14, 12

3   **a**   4, 24   **b**   5, 60   **c**   14, 84
    d   4, 160   **e**   8, 504   **f**   12, 168

4   **a** $\frac{4}{5}$ **b** $1\frac{1}{2}$ **c** $\frac{4}{7}$
    d $\frac{1}{6}$ **e** $\frac{15}{17}$ **f** $\frac{9}{23}$
    g $1\frac{42}{289}$

5   For example, 4096 or 400.

N5.3HW Mental methods

1   **a**   1, 3, 17, 51
    b   1, 2, 3, 4, 6, 8, 9, 12, 18, 24, 36, 72
    c   1, 2, 3, 6, 9, 18, 27, 54, 81, 162
    d   1, 2, 3, 5, 6, 7, 10, 14, 15, 21, 30, 35, 42, 70, 105, 210

2   **a**   201   **b**   9.2
    c   28   **d**   21

3   **a**   2.3, 6, 12   **b**   3.6, 12, 7.5

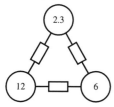 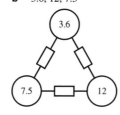

4   **a**   Divisible by both 4 and 3.
    b   15: 5 and 3
        18: 9 and 2 or 6 and 3, etc.

N5.4HW Standard written calculations

1   **a**   10.22 m
    b   36.5 m
    c   292 m

2   Approx. 27 million, to the nearest million.

N5.5HW Standard written division

1   **a**   4.3   **b**   24.4
    c   12.3   **d**   16.8
    e   27.3   **f**   27.1

2   **a**   429.1 ÷ 7   **b**   8.43 ÷ 3 = 2.81

3   35 ÷ 24

N5.6HW Using equivalent fractions

1   Student's own work.

2 $\frac{7}{12}, \frac{3}{5}, \frac{5}{8}, \frac{13}{20}, \frac{2}{3}, \frac{7}{10}, \frac{17}{24}, \frac{11}{15}, \frac{3}{4}, \frac{23}{30}, \frac{5}{6}$

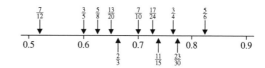

N5.7HW Converting decimals to fractions

There are no unique solutions to this investigation.

N5.8HW Sequences in diagrams

1   **a**   Cashew nuts (96.4 g in total.)
    b   Baked beans, hot chocolate, cashew nuts
    c   32.6 g

2   Student's own work.

N5 SAT Level 4

a £40   **b** £5.96   **c** 8   **d** 3   **e** 11

N5 SAT Level 5

a £123.50   **b** 15

CORE

D3 Analysing statistics

D3.1HW Planning data collection
There are no unique solutions to this investigation.

D3.2HW Statistical diagrams

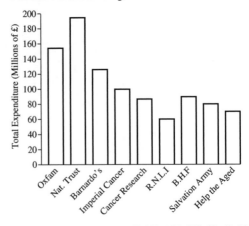

1 Bar chart with heights 155, 190, 125, 102, 88, 60, 93, 79, 63
2 Student's own answer.

D3.3HW Comparing data
1 a

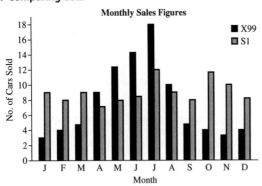

b The X99 is the open-topped sports car as more were sold in the summer.

2

D3.4HW Describing data
1 A: 6.6, 5, 5
   B: 7.3, 4, 3
   C: 5.25, 6, 7
   D: 4.75, 3.65, no mode
   E: 30.2, 27, 17 and 31
   F: 151.7, 152, 147 and 152
   G: 4.3, 4.35, no mode
2 26 seems out of place
   4.2, 3.5, 3
   The median and mode change. The mode is the best average.

D3.5HW Communicating findings
There are no unique solutions to this investigation.

D3 SAT Level 4
a i Tuesday
   ii Friday
b 0.25 cm
c i 1.5 cm
   ii 15 mm

D3 SAT Level 5
a Missing entries: 94, 8, 94, 101, 7
b 198 cm

D4 Probability experiments

D4.1HW Theoretical probability

1 a $\frac{1}{100}$ b $\frac{9}{100}$ c $\frac{9}{100}$
   d $\frac{1}{10}$ e $\frac{1}{2}$ f $\frac{33}{100}$

2 The blue 24 has a $\frac{1}{100}$ chance of winning. The colour is irrelevant. Keith is wrong to complain.

3 a $\frac{1}{9}$ b $\frac{2}{9}$ c $\frac{1}{3}$
   d $\frac{2}{3}$ e $\frac{4}{9}$ f $\frac{5}{9}$

4 $\frac{2}{21}$

D4.3HW Experimental probability

1 A is the data from the unfair dice (it is biased towards 2)
   B is the data from the fair dice (the data is spread more evenly)
   C is the made-up data (the data is too uniform)

2 a Not enough fish measured.
   b Biased sample − he might not be able to get through if people are using the Internet. He should use a different method to contact people.
   c Presumably, most people in the shopping mall enjoy being there. She should ask people in a different location.

3 Student's own work. Measures could include checking winners and winning numbers for a large number of previous weeks, and doing random checks over a number of years.

D4 SAT Level 4
a Various answers b 1 c Various answers d White

D4.2HW Experimental probability

1 a 1: $\frac{13}{50}$ 2: $\frac{12}{25}$ b 1: $\frac{1}{6}$ 2: $\frac{8}{51}$
      3: $\frac{9}{50}$ 4: $\frac{2}{25}$ 3: $\frac{3}{34}$ 4: $\frac{3}{17}$
                                               5: $\frac{7}{17}$

   c 1: $\frac{1}{20}$ 2: $\frac{73}{80}$ 3: $\frac{3}{80}$

2 Roll dice a large number of times. Record the score. Each number should have roughly the same probability. The greater the number of rolls the more accurate the result.

D4 SAT Level 5
a i $\frac{1}{4}$ ii $\frac{1}{2}$ b i 0 ii $\frac{2}{3}$

A5 Equations and graphs

A5.1HW Solving linear equations

1 a $a = 3$ b $c = 5$ c $m = 2$
   d $r = 4$ e $s = 7$ f $u = 6$
2 a $a = 5$ b $d = 11$ c $n = 8$
3 a $h = 3$ b $i = 8$ c $s = 13$
4 a $a = 2.5$ b $c = 10.5$ c $g = 4.5$
   d $i = 6.5$ e $m = 1.5$
5 a $a = 0$ b $h = 6$ c $m = ^-3$
   d $s = 11$ e $t = 4$
6 a $c = ^-1$ b $i = ^-3$ c $k = 2$
   d $r = ^-4$ e $s = 5$ f $t = ^-6$
7 marcus and his magic maths tricks

A5.3HW Deriving formulae

1 a £16.80
   b £0.4x
   c £0.4($x + 10$) or £(0.4$x + 4$)
   d 55 papers per day

2
Competitor	Time	Position
Solhi	ys	3
Maggie	$y - 3s$	1
Ahmed	$2ys$	6
Mohammed	$2y - 4s$	5
Charlotte	$y - 2s$	2
Ebony	$y + 5s$	4

3 a $4n$ b $4n - 88$
   c $2n - 44$ d $2n - 107$
   e $10n - 287$ f $10n - 452$
   g 348

A5.2HW Using formulae

1 b 80 metres per minute c 100 metres per second
   d 850 kilometres per hour e Student's own answer
2 a 4 cm³, 8 cm³, 12 cm³, 18 cm³, 27 cm³, 48 cm³, 64 cm³
   b 1 cm³, 8 cm³, 27 cm³, 64 cm³

A5.4HW Generating sequences

1 a

   b No. of lines: 6, 11, 16, 21, 26, $5n + 1$
      Multiples of 5: 5, 10, 15, 20, 25, $5n$
      Multiples of 5 + 1: 6, 11, 16, 21, 26, $5n + 1$

      No. of dots: 4, 7, 10, 13, 16, $3n + 1$
      Multiples of 3: 3, 6, 9, 12, 15, $3n$
      Multiples of 3 + 1: 4, 7, 10, 13, 16, $3n + 1$
   c $5n + 1$ lines and $3n + 1$ dots

2 4 counters are added each time.

3 a   b $2n + 6$

CORE

A5.5HW Spot the function
1 a 3, 6, 9, 30
   b 0, 3, 6, 27
   c 3, 6, 9, 30
   d Yes, the first and last machines are equivalent to ×3.
2 a ×5, +5 or +1, ×5
   b $5x + 5$ or $5(x + 1)$
3 a See Q2a
   b See Q2b
   c $5x + 5 = 5(x + 1)$

A5.6HW Graphs of functions
1 Student's own answer
2 3, 6, 9, 13, 17, 19, 20, 19, 16, 10, 9 (to nearest whole number)
3 Higher in 2002.

A5.7HW Graphs of equations
1 a $y = 2x + 2$: ⁻4, ⁻2, 0, 2, 4, 6, 8
      $y = x - 1$: ⁻4, ⁻3, ⁻2, ⁻1, 0, 1, 2

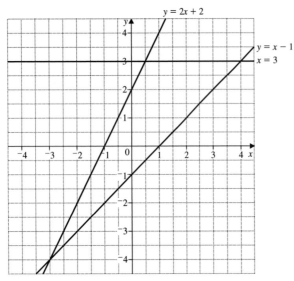

   b (⁻3, ⁻4), (⁻2, ⁻2), (⁻1, 0), (0, 2), (1, 4), (2, 6), (3, 8)
      (⁻3, ⁻4), (⁻2, ⁻3), (⁻1, ⁻2), (0, ⁻1), (1, 0), (2, 1), (3, 2)
   c Points from **b** plotted with a straight line through each set
   d Two straight lines
   e (⁻3, ⁻4)
   f Line $x = 3$ drawn
      A scalene triangle is formed.

A5.8HW Linear graphs
1 a Line a is $y = 2x + 4$.   Line b is $y = 7$.
      Line c is $y = 1 - x$.   Line d is $x = ⁻1$.
   b a – Line goes through 4 on y axis
      b – parallel to x axis
      c – Negative gradient
      d – Parallel to y-axis
2 Line a is $y = x$.
   Line b is $y = x + 3$.
   Line c is $y = x - 2$.
   Line d is $y = 3$.
   Line e is $x = 5$.
   Line f is $y = 3 - x$.

A5 SAT Level 4

a	50	b	16	c	10	d	10
e	27	f	7	g	100	h	10

A5 SAT Level 5
a The grey tiles   **b** 1 black, 36 grey
c 20   **d** $1 + 6N$
e Three correct patterns with tiles totalling 5, 9 and 13

S5 | Polygons

S5.1HW Constructing triangles
Student's own answer.

S5.2HW Constructing quadrilaterals
1 Student's own answer

2 **a** Student's own answer   **b** Angle R = 100°   **c** Student's own answer.

    d Parallelogram   Rectangle   Pentagon

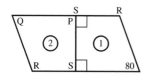 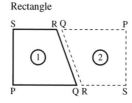 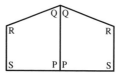

    e Parallelogram   Rectangle   Pentagon
       No lines of symmetry   2 lines of symmetry   1 line of symmetry
       Rotational symmetry 2   Rotational symmetry 2   No rotational symmetry

 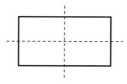 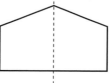

    f

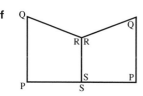

    g Investigation (Keep putting matching sides together to obtain different shapes)

S5.3HW Constructing 2-D shapes
1 **a** i and iv
   b ii and iii

2 **a**   **b**

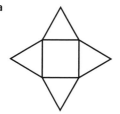 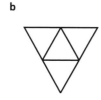

other possibilities

S5.4HW Properties of triangles and quadrilaterals
Square: 4 sides of equal length, opposite sides parallel, adjacent sides at right angles, rotational symmetry of order 4, 4 lines of reflection symmetry, all angles 90°

Rectangle: opposite sides equal and parallel, adjacent sides at right angles, rotational symmetry of order 2, 2 lines of reflection symmetry, all angles 90°

Rhombus: 4 sides of equal length, opposite sides parallel, opposite angles equal, rotational symmetry of order 2, 2 lines of reflection symmetry

Parallelogram: opposite sides equal and parallel, opposite angles equal, rotational symmetry of order 2, no reflection symmetry

Kite: two pairs of adjacent equal sides, all angles convex, one pair of opposite angles equal, no rotational symmetry, one line of reflection symmetry

Arrowhead: two pairs of adjacent equal sides, three convex angles and one concave angle, one pair of opposite angles equal, no rotational symmetry, one line of reflection symmetry

Trapezium: one pair of opposite sides parallel, no equal sides or angles, no rotational symmetry, no reflection symmetry

Isosceles Trapezium: one pair of opposite sides parallel, the other pair of opposite sides equal, two pairs of adjacent equal angles, no rotational symmetry, one line of reflection symmetry

CORE

S5.5HW Properties of polygons

a **5-sided arrowhead:** no rotational symmetry, one line of reflection symmetry

T-shape: no rotational symmetry, one line of reflection symmetry

Square: rotational symmetry order 4, 4 lines of reflection symmetry

b Rectangle

Rotational symmetry 2

d

Sketch	Name	Number of lines of symmetry	Order of rotational symmetry
Rectangle	Rectangle	2	2
		None	2
		None	2
	T shape	1	None
	U-shape	1	None
	Cross	2	2
	T shape	1	None
	S shape	0	2
	I shape	2	2
	Cross on a base	1	0
	Cross	1	0

S5.6HW Tessellating polygons

Rectangle   Parallelogram

 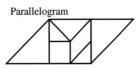

Trapezium with 2 right-angles   Isosceles trapezium

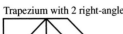 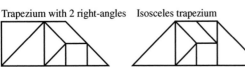 

Triangle

Irregular hexagon

 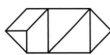

Irregular pentagon

S5 SAT Level 4

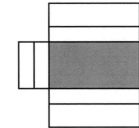

S5 SAT Level 5

a Triangle drawn correctly (9 cm ±2 mm, 51° and 74° ±2°)

b Trapezium drawn correctly (121° ±2°, 2.5 cm ±2 mm and trapezium completed)

A1 Sequences and functions

A1.1HW Introducing sequences

1 Examples are:
2, 4, 6, 8, 10, … $6\frac{1}{4}, 6\frac{1}{2}, 7, 8, 10, …$ 4.096, 5.12, 6.4, 8, 10, …

2 Examples are:
1, 2, 3, 4, 5, …   1, 2, 4, 8, 16, …   1, 2, 4, 7, 11, …

3 **a** 1, 3, 9, 27, 81   **b** 80, 40, 20, 10, 5
  c 5, 10, 15, 20, 25   **d** 1, 8, 27, 64, 125

4 **a** Start with 1, 1 and add the previous two terms.
  b Examples are:
    the arrangement of scales on a fir-cone
    the spiralling florets of a sunflower
    the way leaves are arranged on a plant shoot
  c 3, 5, 9, 17, …

5 **a** 1 6 15 20 25 6 1
  b Positive integers, triangular numbers. Rows of 1s.
    Series of whole numbers 1, 2, 3, 4, 5.

A1.3HW Sequences in diagrams

1 **A** **a**

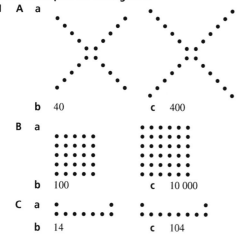

  b 40   **c** 400

  B **a**

  b 100   **c** 10 000

  C **a**

  b 14   **c** 104

2 All square jigsaws have 4 corner pieces.
There are $100 - 2 = 98$ edge pieces along each edge, giving
$98 \times 4 = 392$ edge pieces in total.
There are $(100 - 2)2 = 9604$ middle pieces.
There are $1002 = 10\ 000$ pieces in total and
$4 + 392 + 9604 = 10\ 000$, so all pieces have been counted.

A1.5HW Finding the function

1 **a** 41
  b A and C
  c A and C. $n \times 2 + 1 = 2n + 1$. $(n +) \times 2 = 2n + 1$
  d 9

2 Machine 2, as the output is always even.

3 $\times 3, -1$

A1.2HW Sequences and rules

1 **a** 5, 8, 11, 14, 17   **b** 17, 13, 9, 5, 1
  c 5, 6, 7, 8, 9   **d** 7, 10, 13, 16, 19

2 Start at 5 and add 4; Multiply by 4 and add 1
Start at 7 and add 9; Multiply by 9 and subtract 2
Start at 20 and add 19; Multiply by 19 and add 1
Start at $\frac{1}{2}$ and add $\frac{1}{2}$; Multiply by $\frac{1}{2}$

3 **a** True, the position-to-term rule is 'Multiply by 3 and add 1' and
    97 is one more than a multiple of 3.
  b False, 170 is not a square number.
  c If the sequence starts with an odd number all terms will be
    odd − False.
    If the sequence starts with an even number, all terms will be
    even − True.

4 **a** Start at 1 and add 2; Multiply by 2 and subtract 1
  b Start at 1 and add the next odd number; Multiply the position
    by itself

A1.4HW Function machines

1 **a** position → multiply by 4 → term
  b position → add 10 → term
  c position → multiply by 5 → add 1 → term
  d position → divide by 4 → term

2 **a** 1, 4, 9, 16, 25, 36, 49, 64, 81, 100, 121, 144, 169, 196, 225
    These are the square numbers.
  b 1, 8, 27, 64, 125, 216   These are the cube numbers.
  c 1, 3, 6, 10, 15, 21, 28, 36, 45, 55

3 **a** Add 1 then divide by 3
  b Cube then double it

A1.6HW Functions and algebra

1 **B** $\frac{z}{3}, \frac{z}{3} - 4$ **C** $3x, 3x + 1,$
  D $w^2, 10w^2, 10w^2 + 7, 5(10w^2 + 7)$

2 **a** $x \to \times 6 \to 6x \to -1 \to 6x - 1$
  b $x \to +4 \to x + 4 \to \div 5 \to \dfrac{(x + 4)}{5}$
  c $x \to \text{cubed} \to x^3 \to -2 \to x^3 - 2$
  d $x \to \text{squared} \to x^2 \to \times 2 \to 2x^2 \to +7 \to 2x^2 + 7 \to \times 3$
    $\to 3(2x^2 + 7)$
  e $x \to \times 5 \to 5x \to +1 \to 5x + 1 \to \div 4 \to \dfrac{(5x + 1)}{4} \to -3$
    $\to \dfrac{(5x + 1)}{4} - 3 \to \times 10 \to 10\left(\dfrac{(5x + 1)}{4} - 3\right)$

3 **a** For example: For $x \to \times$ itself, the expression in the tail is x^2
  b For example: For $x \to +5 \to \times$ itself $\to \times \frac{1}{4}$,
    the expression in the tail is $(x + 5)^2$.

4 **a** Examples are: $+1, \times 10$ etc.
  b Examples are: $\times$ itself, $\div$ itself
  c Examples are: $+1, +3$ etc.

A1 SAT Level 5

a The grey tiles   **b** 1 black, 36 grey
c 200   **d** $1 + 6N$
e Three correct patterns with tiles totalling 5, 9 and 13

A1 SAT Level 6

a 64 grey, 4 black   **b** 256 grey, 4 black
c P^2 grey, 4 black   **d** $T = P^2 + 4$

EXTENSION

N1 — Number calculations

N1.1HW Place value and ordering

1 a I, II, III, IV, V, VI, VII, VIII, IX, X
  b Student's own answer.
  c V (5), XX (20), XL (40), L (50), LV (55), LXXI (71), C (100)

N1.2HW Negative numbers I

1 $18 + 41 + {}^-9 + 21 = 71$
2 ${}^-17 + {}^-24 + {}^-13 + 11 = {}^-43$

N1.3HW Negative numbers II

1 a 7
  b 2
  c ${}^-6$
  d ${}^-2$
  e ${}^-6$
  f 24
  g Examples are:
     $2, 2, {}^-9$
     ${}^-3, 3, 4$
     ${}^-2, {}^-3, {}^-6$
  h 6

2 ${}^-2, {}^-5$
   $5, {}^-10, 15, {}^-25$
   ${}^-6, {}^-18, 30$
   ${}^-3, 6, {}^-9$
   ${}^-4, {}^-10, {}^-8$

3 a ${}^-21$
  b ${}^-12$
  c ${}^-2$
  d ${}^-2$
  e 18
  f 22
  g ${}^-8$
  h ${}^-2$

N1.4HW Mental strategies

Students are asked to design a poster on mental addition and subtraction of decimals.

N1.5HW Add and subtract decimals

4 $7.3, 7.3, 7.3, 7.3$
   $0, 0, 0, 0$
   This took 4 steps.

   If the numbers at the ends of a diagonal are both larger than the numbers at the end of the other diagonal it will take 4 steps. Other investigations may have other solutions.

N1.6HW Using a calculator

1 a $4.7\ (4.5 - 5.0)$ b $0.5\ (0.4 - 0.6)$ c ${}^-4.5\ ({}^-4\ \text{to}\ {}^-5)$
2 a 4 hours 31 minutes
  b $1°11'0''$ or 1.183333333
3 a 32p has been keyed as 32 instead of 0.32.
  b The display '8.1' should have been interpreted as £8 and 10p.
  c £9.58 has been added not subtracted.
4 a 11.111; check: $7.5 + 3.5 = 11$
  b ${}^-5.439$; check: $16 - (3 + 4 + 8 + 6) = 16 - 21 = {}^-5$
  c 29.175; check: $24 - {}^-5 = 24 + 5 = 29$
  d 0.292971468; check: $\dfrac{(9-5)}{(9+5)} = \dfrac{4}{14} = \dfrac{2}{7} = 0.29$

N1 SAT Level 5

a Various answers, for example 4 and ${}^-1$
b i Various answers, for example ${}^-7$ and 6
   ii Various answers
c ${}^-4$
d ${}^-7, {}^-5, {}^-3$ Total $= {}^-15$

N1 SAT Level 6

a 7
b ${}^-8, {}^-10$
c $9, {}^-11$
d ${}^-8, 6$

EXTENSION

S1   Perimeter and area

S1.1HW Perimeter and area

1   $81\,cm^2$

2   Area = $24\,m^2$, Perimeter = 28 m

3   Maximum area = $100\,m^2$ (10 m by 10 m)

4   Just over $80\,m^2$, because there is slightly more pond outside an 8 m by 10 m rectangle than is missing inside the rectangle.

S1.3HW Measurements and scales

There are no unique solutions to this investigation.

S1 SAT Level 5

a   i $252\,cm^2$ ii   252   b $n^2, 2n, 6$

S1.2HW More perimeter and area

1   For example:

    25 m × 40 m = $1000\,m^2$

2   a $30\,cm^2$ b $12.5\,mm^2$ c $30\,cm^2$

3   6.3 cm

4   a $30\,mm^2$ b $15\,m^2$ c $24\,cm^2$

    d $16\,cm^2$ e $9\,mm^2$

S1.4HW Three dimensional shapes

1   6 faces, 8 vertices, 12 edges   2   6 faces, 8 vertices, 12 edges

    Surface area = $96\,cm^2$ Surface area = $62\,in^2$

    Volume = $64\,cm^3$ Volume = $30\,in^3$

3   6 faces, 8 vertices, 12 edges   4   5 faces, 6 vertices, 9 edges

    Surface area = $50.86\,cm^2$ Surface area = $74\,cm^2$

    Volume = $17.325\,cm^3$ Volume = $35\,cm^3$

5   4 faces, 4 vertices, 6 edges

    Surface area = $28\,cm^2$

S1 SAT Level 6

a $2.5\,cm^2$ b   10 cm   c   Various answers

N2   Fractions, decimals and percentages

N2.1HW Understanding fractions

1, 2 There are no unique solutions to this investigation.

3   For example:

    $\frac{1}{2}, \frac{1}{4}, \frac{1}{6}$ and $\frac{1}{12}$

4   For example:

    $\frac{1}{2}, \frac{1}{4}, \frac{1}{5}$ and $\frac{1}{20}$

N2.3HW Add and subtract fractions

1   There are no unique solutions to this investigation.

2   Some vehicles may not fit.

3   18 vehicles (21 without gaps)

N2.5HW Fractions of an amount

1   $\frac{7}{2} \times 14, \frac{7}{3} \times 21$ etc.

2   $\frac{1}{7} \times 44, \frac{2}{7} \times 22$ etc.

3   a $22\frac{2}{3}\,cm$ b $7\frac{1}{11}\,kg$

    c   £18   d $45\frac{1}{5}$

    e $\frac{1}{105}$ f $\frac{27}{64}$

    g $\frac{2}{135}$

N2 SAT Level 5

a   £4.50   b   £45   c   35%   d   £5

N2.2HW Equivalent fractions

1   a $a = \frac{7}{16}, b = \frac{1}{2}$ b $a = \frac{3}{4}, b = \frac{11}{12}$ c $a = \frac{13}{32}, b = \frac{7}{16}, c = \frac{15}{32}$

3   $\frac{16}{21}$

4   a $3\frac{1}{2}$ b $1\frac{4}{13}$ c $2\frac{17}{18}$ d $\frac{5}{24}$

5   $\frac{23}{3}, 3\frac{8}{9}, 3\frac{5}{6}, \frac{16}{7}, 2\frac{1}{7}, \frac{16}{9}$

N2.4HW Fractions and decimals

1   If two tables have the same amount of chocolate, each person sits at the lowest numbered table.

    Person 1 sits at table 3   Person 6 sits at table 3

    Person 2 sits at table 2   Person 7 sits at table 1

    Person 3 sits at table 3   Person 8 sits at table 2

    Person 4 sits at table 1   Person 9 sits at table 3

    Person 5 sits at table 2   Person 10 sits at table 1

2   Person 11 sits at table 2   Person 14 sits at table 2

    Person 12 sits at table 3   Person 15 sits at table 3

    Person 13 sits at table 1   Person 16 sits at table 1

N2.6HW Fractions, decimals and percentages

There are no unique solutions to this investigation.

N2 SAT Level 6

a $\frac{7}{16}$ b   £60

EXTENSION

D1 — Statistics and probability

D1.1HW Finding the average

1 a i Median = 2°C, mode = 3°C, range = 6°C
  ii The median, as the mode is too high.
  iii Night temperatures, weather forecaster.
 b i Median = 11 mm, mode = 10 mm and 11 mm, range = 7 mm
  ii The median, as there are two modes.
    The mode does cover half the values in the middle range.
  iii Widths of components, quality controller in a factory.
 c i Median = 3, mode = 2.5, range = 1.2
  ii The median, as the mode is too low.
  iii Weights of bags of potatoes, market stall holder.

2 a i Median = 6, mode = 5 and 7
  ii The median, as there are two modes.
    The mode does cover most common sizes.
 b i Median = 107 cm, mode = 125 cm
  ii The median, as the mode is too high.
 c i Median = 81.9p, mode = 79.9p and 81.9p
  ii The median, as there are two modes.
    The mode does cover half the values in the middle range.
 d i Median = 45 mins, mode = 30 mins and 1 hour
  ii The median, as there are two modes.

3 March: median = 32p, mode = 30p and 35p
  April: median = 30p, no mode

D1.2HW The mean

1 a 10.625
 b 22.1 cm
 c 10.15 s
 d 49.5 kg
2 a 5.4
 b 44.9 kg
3 a 10.2 s
 b 28 pins
 c 23 films
 d For example: 9, 9, 9
       8, 9, 10

D1.3HW Interpreting diagrams

1 Student's own answer.
2 a Just under 4 million
 b 4 + 5.5 = 9.5 million
3 Approx. 61 million
4 a $\dfrac{3.5}{61}$ = 5.7%. 5−6% is acceptable.
 b $\dfrac{6}{61}$ = 10%
5 Provision of schools, pensions, housing, healthcare etc.

D1.4HW Introducing probability

1 a Equally likely, same number of black and white beads.
 b Boys are more likely to win, more white beads than black.
 c Boys are certain to win, there are no black beads.
2 A: $\frac{1}{2}$
  B: $\frac{2}{5}$
  C: 0
  D: $\frac{1}{2}$
  E: $\frac{3}{5}$
  F: 1
3 a A lot of balls, with one white and the rest black.
 b Any number of balls, all of which are black.
 c A large odd number of balls with one more white ball than black balls.
 d Any even number of balls, half of which are black and half white.

D1.5HW Calculating probabilities

1 Possible outcomes:
  FAT, FAE, FTA, FTE, FEA, FET, **AFT**, AFE, ATF, **ATE**, AEF, AET, TFA, TFE, TAF, TAE, TEF, **TEA**, EFA, EFT, EAF, **EAT**, ETF, ETA
  There is a $\frac{5}{24}$ chance of getting in free.
  (Other words possible are EFT, TAE, TEF, but these are not common usage.)

2 Possible outcomes:
  FAT, FAE, TEF, **ATE**
  There is a $\frac{1}{2}$ chance of getting in free.

D1.6HW Experimental probability

When subtracting the scores, the most common value is one.
There is no unique solution to this investigation.
Experimental results will differ.

D1 SAT Level 5

a September
b May, June, October, November, December
c January, February, December

D1 SAT Level 6

a 30%, $\frac{3}{10}$, $\frac{6}{20}$, 0.3
b i $\frac{9}{20}$ **ii** 45%

A2   Expressions and formulae

A2.1HW Using letter symbols

1   **a**   No
    b   No

2   **a**   28
    b   163
    c   600
    d   29
    e $^-2$
    f   22
    g   104
    h   216

3   **a** $d = 1, d = 6, d = 6$
    b $d = 6, d = 1, d = 1$

A2.2HW Using the rules of algebra

1   **a**   Using four large negative numbers gives a small total.
       Using four large positive numbers gives a large total.
       The order of the numbers does not matter.
    b   Four equal numbers gives a total of eight times the starting number.
       Four consecutive numbers gives a total of eight times the smallest starting number plus twelve.
    c   Yes. Double the sum of the starting numbers.
    d   Starting numbers p, q, r, s give a total of $2p + 2q + 2r + 2s$ or $2(p + q + r + s)$.

2   **a** $n + (n + 1) + (n + 2) = 3n + 3 = 3(n + 3)$, which is a multiple of 3
    b $n + (n + 1) + (n + 2) + (n + 3) + (n + 4) = 5n + 10$, which is 10 more than a multiple of 5

A2.3HW Simplifying expressions

1   Student's own answer

2   **a** $12x + 24p$
    b $2h + 8k$
    c $7a + 6b + d$
    d $60a - 40b$

3   Squares: $9p + 2q, 11p - 5q$
    Circle: $5p - 3q$

A2.4HW Simplifying harder expressions

$p + 3q, abc, 10b, 12k$

$3k, 20pq, \dfrac{p}{7}, \dfrac{b}{6}, 40ac$

Cannot be simplified, $12p$, Cannot be simplified, $6c + 13$, Cannot be simplified

Cannot be simplified, Cannot be simplified, Cannot be simplified, w^2, Cannot be simplified

Cannot be simplified, $5q + 8w$, Cannot be simplified, $2ab$, Cannot be simplified

$2m, 2abc, 3q, 44dep, 7x + 18y$

$6b, 2x, 9x - 20, 2a, 4xy$

$13b^2 + b, 12c^2, 10cdpq, 3m^3, 2m^3$

$4m^2, 30x^3, 3ab, 10k^3, 15 - 10y$

This hidden message is HI.

A2.5HW Using formulae

1   144°

2   **a**   £170
    b $P = 50 + 30n$

3   **a** $T = 40W + 20$
    b   7 kg

4   165 matches

5   **a** $S = n + 2$, where S = number of shaded tiles and n = pattern number
    b $T = 4P + 16$

A2 SAT Level 5

a   Barry $a + 2$, Cindy $4a$
b   Ali $b - 2$, Cindy $4(b - 2)$
c $\dfrac{c}{4} + 2$

A2 SAT Level 6

a $n \div 2$
b n^2
c $2n$
d   Various answers, for example $5n$

EXTENSION

| **S2** | **Angles and shapes** |

S2.1HW Finding angles
1   105°. The angles added are equal to the answer.
2   60°
3   70°
4   40°
5   129°
6   40°

S2.3HW Coordinates and shapes
1   (⁻4, ⁻3)
    Area = 30 square units
    Perimeter = 22 units
2   **a**   (5, 2)
    b   (5, 0) or (⁻1, ⁻2)
    c   For example: (1, 1). This arrowhead would not be symetrical.
    d   No, it is not possible to join the three given points to make two
        perpendicular edges.
3   **a**   (⁻5, 3)
    b   Area = 8 square units
        Perimeter = 18 units
4   **a**   (⁻8, 3), (⁻8, ⁻2), (2, 3) or (2, ⁻2)
    b   12.5 square units
5   **a**   (3, ⁻3) and (3, 3) or (⁻9, ⁻3) and (⁻9, 3)
    b   Area = 36 square units
        Perimeter = 24 units
6   Student's own answer.

S2.2HW Angles and lines
1   **a**   PQ and SR
    b   PS and SR or PQ and PS.

2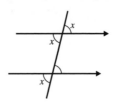

3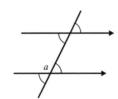

4   **a** 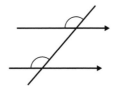   **b**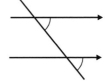

    c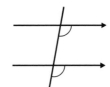

5   **a** 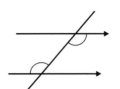   **b**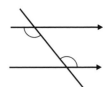

    c

6   **a** $a = 88°$
    b $b = 68°$
    c $c = 120°$

S2 SAT Level 5
a   Q
b   angle within ±2°
c   **i** 38°   **ii** 135°

S2 SAT Level 6
a $a = 100°, b = 140°, c = 120°$
b $d = 50°, e = 130°$
c   60

EXTENSION

D2 Handling data

D2.1HW Discussing statistical methods
1 Secondary data
2 Primary data, consumer survey
3 Secondary data could include the number of males/females in this age group, spending patterns for this age group etc.

They could carry out a survey of this age group and parents of this age group. This would help them find out what design features the target audience would like to see.

The easiest way to contact this age group would be through schools, but they may not be happy for their pupils to have mobile phones.

D2.2HW Collecting data
Student's own answer

D2.3HW Organising the data
1 Time: 20–24, 25–29, 30–34, 35–39, 40–44, 45–49, 50–54
Frequency: 3, 5, 7, 11, 14, 7, 3
2 0–10, 11–20, 21–30, 31–40, 41–50, 51–60
Frequency: 9, 4, 3, 6, 8, 5

D2.4HW Displaying your results
1 Frequency diagram with frequencies: 3, 5, 7, 11, 14, 7, 3
2 Pie chart with angles:
0 pupils 19° 1 pupil 49° 2 pupils 68° 3 pupils 117°
4 pupils 78° 5 pupils 29°
A pie chart compares each section with the whole.
A bar chart gives a better idea of the original data and actual values.

D2.5HW Interpreting diagrams
1 a 32
  b 9
  c 11
  d No, all you can say is that the youngest teacher is between 20 and 30 years old.
2 The most popular transport is cycling for boys, whereas it is walking for girls, etc.

D2 SAT Level 5
a 20%–30%
b 2 to 3 million
c The total number of people in each country needs to be taken into account
d Pie chart with angles 72°, 126°, 90°, 72°

D2 SAT Level 6
a Pie chart with angles 54°, 234° and 72° (±2°)
b 24

EXTENSION

N3 | Multiplication and division

N3.1HW Number and measures

1 a 7800　b 0.9　c 89　d 0.094
2 a 10　b 100　c 100
3 a 0.1　b 0.01　c 0.01
4 a 0.6　b 700　c 0.03　d 20
5 a 80　b 0.01　c 661　d 222
6 a 4 000 000 cm²　b 600 000 cm²
　c 7000 cm²
7 a 600 000 000 mm²　b 600 000 mm²
　c 500 000 mm²
8 a 8000 mm²　b 5 600 000 mm²
　c 120 mm²
9 10 rods of length 0.21 m (total length 2.1 m compared with 2 m for 2000 cm ÷ 10)
10 a 0.35　b 12　c 0.9　d 0.296
11 10 cm × 10 cm = 100 cm²
　1 m × 1 m = 100 cm × 100 cm = 10 000 cm²
12 a 5 000 000 mm²　b 400 000 mm²
　c 6000 mm²　d 310 000 mm²

N3.2HW Powers and operations
There are no unique solutions to this investigation

N3.3HW Mental methods
There are no unique solutions to this investigation
$19 \times 17 = 1649$

N3.4HW Multiplying by partitioning

1 b 10 005
2 b 41 720
3 b 35 476
4 b 22 518
5 b 36 582
6 b 32 565
7 b 4590
8 b 40 515
9 b 16.32
10 b 77.19
11 b 10.45
12 b 1.87
13 b 47.84
14 b 453.18
15 b 328.32
16 b 310.21
17 b 12.19
18 b 243.04
19 b 0.00615
20 b 3.3583

N3.5HW Multiplying on paper

1 3473
2 3 247 255 g or 3247.255 kg
3 13 680 g or 13.68 kg
4 £79.58
5 440
6 £578
7 £521.55
8 359.48 cm
9 £9.88

N3.6HW Dividing on paper

a 50.2
b 80.4
c 2250

N3.7HW Dividing with remainders

1 a The 6th leg.
　b 7000
2 £26.37
3 730, 0.73, 73, 9, 0.9

N3.8HW Calculator methods
There are no unique solutions to this investigation

N3 SAT Level 5
a 52 920 g　　b No, too heavy　　c 8

N3 SAT Level 6
a i 3⁴　ii 3⁴　b 2² and 2⁷

a i 3^4　ii 3^4　b 2^2 and 2^7

EXTENSION

A3   Functions and graphs

A3.1HW Factors, multiples and primes

ACROSS		DOWN	
1	30	1	323
2	169	2	101
3	24	3	23
4	1156	4	165
6	360	5	63
7	965	6	364
9	132	8	43

A3.2HW Patterns in numbers

1   **a**   B   **b**   H
     c   D   **d**   G
     e   A   **f**   I
     g   E   **h**   F
     i   C

2   **a** $T(n) = 4n + 4$
     b $T(n) = 13n - 10$
     c $T(n) = n^2$
     d $T(n) = n^3$
     e $T(n) = \dfrac{1}{2n}$
     f $T(n) = \dfrac{2}{n^2}$
     g $\dfrac{(n + 1)}{(n + 2)}$

A3.3HW Patterns in numbers

1   **a**   Number of dots d: 3, 6, 9, 12   **b** $d = 3n$
     c   One dot is added to each of the three sides of the triangle each time.

2   **a**   Number of tiles n: 1, 4, 9, 16   **b** $n = h^2$
     c   You can rearrange the blocks to make a square.

3   **a**   Number below in calendar n: 8, 9, 10, 11
     b $n = d + 7$
     c   A week (7 days) is added each time.

A3.4HW Functions and rules

1   **a** $n \rightarrow 3n$
     b $n \rightarrow 3n - 1$
     c $n \rightarrow n^2 + 1$
     d $n \rightarrow (n - 1)^2$

2   **a** y: ⁻5, ⁻3, ⁻1, 1, 3
     b y: ⁻8, ⁻3, 2, 7, 12
     c y: 64, 25, 4, 1, 16
     d y: 11, $3\frac{1}{2}$, 1, $3\frac{1}{2}$, 11

A3.5HW Graphs of functions

1   **a** y: 4, 5, 6
        Points (1, 4), (2, 5) and (3, 6) plotted with a line through labelled $y = x + 3$
     b y: 3, 5, 7
        Points (1, 3), (2, 5) and (3, 7) plotted with a line through labelled $y = 2x + 1$
     c y: ⁻1, 2, 5
        Points (1, ⁻1), (2, 2) and (3, 5) plotted with a line through labelled $y = 3x - 4$
     d y: 9, 8, 7
        Points (1, 9), (2, 8) and (3, 7) plotted with a line through labelled $x + y = 10$

2   $y = 2x - 3$, diagonal, (5, 7) $y = 5$, horizontal, (6, 5)
   $x = ⁻2$, vertical, (⁻2, 8) $y = 10 - x$, diagonal, (3, 7)

A3.6HW Using a table of values

1   No, $10 \neq 10 - 3$ when $x = 10$, $y = 7$

2   Examples are:
     $y = x + 4$ $y = 2x + 1$ $y = 3x - 2$

3   **a**   (3, 5)
     b   (7, ⁻2)
     c   (4, 7)

4   **a** $y = 3x + c$ for any value of c
     b $y = mx + c$ for $m > 2$ and any value of c
     c $y = c$ for any value of c
     d   Any equation not of the form $y = mx + c$, e.g. $y = x^2$
     e $y = mx + 4$ for any value of m
     f $y = 5 - x$

A3 SAT Level 5

a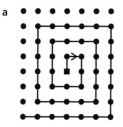

b   12
c $\div 2$
d   9

A3 SAT Level 6

a $x = 8$
b $y = x + 7$
c $y = x - 1$

EXTENSION

S3   Triangles and quadrilaterals

S3.1HW Calculating angles
1   Adjacent angles in a parallelogram sum to 180°. $x = 140°$
2   Angles in a triangle sum to 180°, so the sum of two angles must be less than 180°. $x = 50°$
3   An internal angle and an external angle must sum to 180°. $x = 60°$
4   Angles at a point sum to 360°. $x = 110°$

S3.2HW Angles in shapes
a   108°
b   135°
c   144°

S3.3HW Constructing triangles
1   QR = 3.7 cm, PR = 3.4 cm, angle R = 100°
2   Angle B = 55°, angle C = 83°, BC = 4.2 cm
3   Angle X = 67°, angle Y = 90°, angle Z = 23°
4   The sum of the lengths of two of the sides is less than the length of the third side, so the triangle does not exist.
5   The given angles sum to more than 180° so the triangle does not exist.

S3.4HW Constructing bisectors
Student's own work.

S3.5HW 2-D representations of 3-D shapes
1   Any accurate net of the right-angled triangular prism
2   Sketch of the triangular prism
3   9 edges, 6 vertices, 5 faces
4   Accurate plan, front and side elevations to match view sketched in **2**
5   126 cm^2

Challenge
Student's own work
This is an eight-sided shape made up of equilateral triangles.

S3 SAT Level 5
a   Line 10.5 cm, with angles 80° and 30°
b   About 5.6 cm ($\pm$ 2 mm)
c   About 112 m

S3 SAT Level 6
a   Angles in a triangle add to 180°, so $2 \times 180°$ for a quadrilateral (or other valid explanation)
b   540°
c   900°

EXTENSION

N4 — Percentages, ratio and proportion

N4.1HW Fraction, decimal and percentage equivalents

1 **a** 0.3 **b** $\frac{1}{5}$ **c** Smallest first: $\frac{1}{5}$, 22%, $\frac{7}{25}$, 0.3

2 **a** $\frac{19}{30}$ **b** 0.66 **c** 0.11 **d** $\frac{27}{80}$

3 **a** $0.\dot{1}$
 b $\frac{2}{9} = 0.\dot{2}$
  $\frac{3}{9} = 0.\dot{3}$
  $\frac{4}{9} = 0.\dot{4}$
  $\frac{5}{9} = 0.\dot{5}$
  $\frac{6}{9} = 0.\dot{6}$
  $\frac{7}{9} = 0.\dot{7}$
  $\frac{8}{9} = 0.\dot{8}$
  $\frac{9}{9} = 0.\dot{9}$

 c $0.\dot{9} = 1$
  This is a rounding error.

N4.2HW Finding simple percentages

1 **a** £6.38 **b** 8.75 cm **c** 15.2 kg

2 **a** 37.5% of £17 **b** 35% of 25 cm **c** 76% of 20 kg

3 **a** Percentages are often easier to calculate.
  45% of £88 $= \frac{9}{20}$ of £88 $= \frac{198}{5} = £39.60$
  45% of £88 $=$ (50% of £88) $-$ (5% of £88) $= £44 - £4.40$
   $= £39.60$
 b 2.1 kg
 c 45 cm

4 **a** 25%
 b 75%
 c 37.5%
 d 66.7%

N4.3HW Percentage change

1 14.4% increase, 6.0% decrease to one d.p.

2 **a** £450
 b **i** £162.35
  ii £202.94

N4.4HW Proportion

1 **a** €24.15 **b** £16.77 **c** $20.15
 d £8.38 **e** £6.21

2 **a** £1.89 **b** 3.6 cm
 c 1.5 litre bottle. Cost per litre $= \dfrac{1.30}{1.5} = 87\text{p} < 89\text{p}$

3 **a** 9.1 kg **b** 26.4 pounds
 c Student's own answer **d** 14.5 kg

N4.5HW Introducing ratio

1 1 : 4

2 **a** 10.5 kg **b** 25.7 g

3 £300, £250, £150

4 **a** 100 000 cm **b** 1 : 50 000

N4 SAT Level 5

a 1 : 3 **b** 2 : 3 **c** 1 carton of orange juice

N4 SAT Level 6

a 3.6 g **b** A

A4 — Linear equations

A4.1HW Solving algebraic equations

Across
1 14
3 8
4 10
5 11
6 27
7 3

Down
1 18
2 20
4 11
5 17

A4.2HW Solving harder equations

1 120 **6** 632
2 13 **7** 5
3 9 **8** 47
4 39 **9** 63
5 21 **10** 7

A4.3HW Expanding brackets

1 **a** $24 + 4x$
 b $8x - 40$
 c $16 - 2x$

2 **a** $2(x + 9)$ **b** $3(2x - 7)$
 c $y(y - 3)$ **d** $2q(5p + 2)$

A4.4HW Constructing equations

1 km

A4 SAT Level 5

a $5y + 6$ and $6 + 5y$ **b** Yes (if 10 mints in a packet).

A4 SAT Level 6

a 3 **b** **i** $2y + 5 = 23 - y$ **ii** 6

EXTENSION

S4 Transformations

S4.1HW Reflection

1

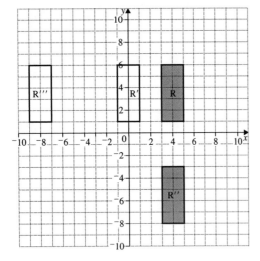

2

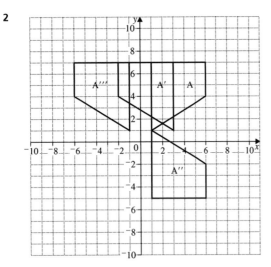

3 **a** and **b**

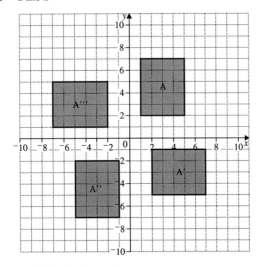

c Reflection in $x = 2$

d Reflection in $y = {}^-1$

S4.2HW Enlargement

1

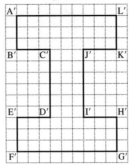

2

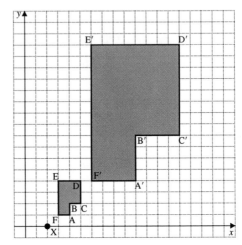

3

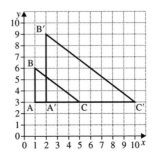

4

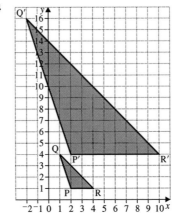

© OUP 2003: this may be reproduced for class use solely for the purchaser's institute

S4.3HW Translation

1 a $\begin{pmatrix} 3 \\ 2 \end{pmatrix}$

   b $\begin{pmatrix} 4 \\ -2 \end{pmatrix}$

   c $\begin{pmatrix} 0 \\ -4 \end{pmatrix}$

   d $\begin{pmatrix} 9 \\ -13 \end{pmatrix}$

2

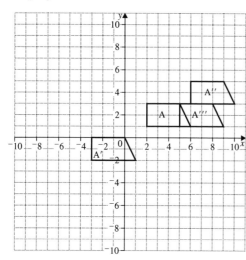

3

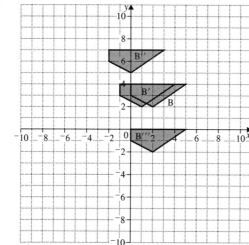

S4.5HW Symmetry

There are no unique solutions to this investigation.

S4 SAT Level 5

a, b, c and d Various answers

S4 SAT Level 6

a B1 → Rotate 90° clockwise (again)
   B2 → Reflect vertical
b A2 → Rotate 90° clockwise (again)
   B1 → Reflect vertical, then rotate 90° clockwise
   B2 → Rotate 90° clockwise

S4.4HW Rotation

1 a–c

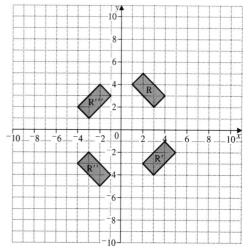

   d Rotation through 90° clockwise (or 270° anticlockwise) about the origin
   e Rotation through 180° about the origin

2 a–c

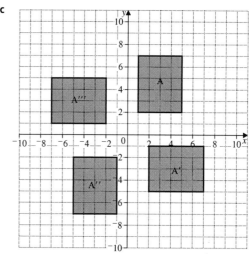

   d Rotation through 90° clockwise (or 270° anticlockwise) about the origin
   e Rotation through 180° about the origin

S4.6HW Transformations

1 a–f and h

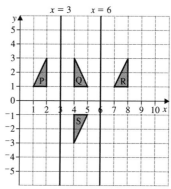

   g Translation $\begin{pmatrix} 6 \\ 0 \end{pmatrix}$

   i Rotation through 180° about (3, 0)

2 A R is the result of two reflections in parallel lines or one translation.

   B S is the result of two reflections in perpendicular lines or one rotation through 180° about (3, 0).

EXTENSION

N5	**More number calculations**

N5.1HW Rounding
1 a Carme
  b Charon
  c 22 580 000 km
2 a 129 000, 181 000, 21 200 000, 191 000, 138 000, 75 000,
     59 000, 1 883 000, 295 000, 22 600 000, 20 000, 50 000
  b They are all over a million, so may have already been rounded
     to the nearest thousand
3 a i   0.498, 2.520, 16.689, 6.387
     ii 0.50, 2.52, 16.69, 6.39
     iii 0.5, 2.5, 16.7, 6.4
     iv 0, 3, 17, 6
  b 6.5 days

N5.2HW Factors, multiples and primes
192, 228, 264, 336, 372, 408, 444, 480, 516, 552, 624, 660, 732, 804,
840, 912
The rest of this investigation has no unique solution.

N5.3HW Multiplying and dividing mentally
1 165, 495, 132, 627
2 a 2, 3, 4, 5, 6, 7, 8, 9, 10, 12, 13, 14, 15, 18, 20, 21, 24, 28, 30
  b 2, 3, 4, 5, 6, 8, 10, 12, 15, 16, 19, 20, 24, 30
  c 2, 3, 4, 5, 6, 8, 9, 10, 12, 15, 16, 18, 19, 20, 24, 27, 30
  d None. It is a prime number.

N5.4HW Standard written multiplication
1 £344.45
2 Adults £2.76, Children £1.62, OAP/Students £1.91
3 a 108 m
  b 651.56 m²

N5.5HW Standard written division
1 a 6.5
  b 1.0
  c 0.9
  d 17.1
  e 5.5
  f 9.1
  g 0.4
  h 3.1
  i 3.2
  j 10.4
2 a 28.84
  b 1.13
  c 1.63
  d 0.14
  e 4.11
  f 9.93
  g 0.07
  h 0.17
  i 0.01
  j 0.61
3 a 20
  b 33
  c 41
  d 12

N5.6HW Using equivalent fractions
1 7.4, 5.4, 7.25, 3.5
2 $\frac{14}{4}, \frac{49}{9}, \frac{58}{8}, \frac{37}{5}$
3 $7\frac{2}{5}, 5\frac{4}{9}, 7\frac{1}{4}, 3\frac{1}{2}$
4 $3\frac{9}{10}$
5 $23\frac{107}{180}$
6 GOLDFISH

N5.7HW Converting fractions, decimals and percentages
1 $\frac{1}{2} = 0.5$, $42.5\% = 0.425$, $\frac{3}{5} = 0.6$, $3.213\% = 0.03213$, $54\% = 0.54$,
   $\frac{7}{9} = 0.78$, $\frac{5}{6} = 0.83$, $\frac{34}{37} = 0.918$, $0.83 + 0.8 + 0.918 = 2.55$ (to 2 d.p.)

2 ELEPHANT
   GIRAFFE
   ZEBRA

N5.8HW Calculating parts of quantities
1 a £80
  b £40
  c £20
2 a £140
  b £280
3 a £16.32
  b £109.57
  c £68.48

N5 SAT Level 5
a $10\% \rightarrow 24$, $5\% \rightarrow 12$, $2\frac{1}{2}\% \rightarrow 6$ so $17\frac{1}{2}\% \rightarrow 42$
b 182

N5 SAT Level 6
49

EXTENSION

D3 Analysing statistics

D3.1HW Planning the data collection
There are no unique solutions to this investigation

D3.3HW Comparing data using diagrams
1 Lewis' and Martha's charts show actual values, whereas Debbie's chart shows proportions.
2 Lewis' and Martha's charts redrawn as a pie charts, or Debbie's chart redrawn as a bar chart.
3 Lewis saw all types of vehicle, but mainly cars, so he was probably at a main road.
 Debbie mainly saw bicycles and motorbikes, so she was probably at a minor country road.
 The high volume of vans and lorries, and the lack of bicycles suggests Martha was at a motorway.

D3.5 Communicating results
Student's own work

Passage 1		**Passage 2**	
Range	= 8	Range	= 8
Median	= 4	Median	= 4
Mean	= 4.08	Mean	= 4.84
Mode	= 3	Mode	= 4

Same range and median. The mean is higher in passage 2

D3 SAT Level 5
a Missing entries: 94, 8, 94, 101, 7
b 198 cm

D3.2HW Constructing statistical diagrams
1 a Graph of age or year against height.
 b Jon's height is increasing over time.
 c Between 1992 and 1993
 d Three features from:
  The graph rises steadily from 1980 to 1987, as Jon grows steadily.
  The graph rises slowly between 1988 to 1991, when Jon does not grow very much.
  The graph rises sharply between 1992 and 1993 as Jon suddenly has a growth spurt.
  The graph continues to rise, but starts to tail off in 1996 as Jon approaches his full adult height.
2 a Pie chart angles:
  Supermarket 137°
  Sweet shop 61°
  Petrol station 33° (rounded up to make total 360° actually 32°.)
  Local grocer 43°
  Newsagent 72°
  Other 14°
 b Supermarket
 c Market stall, for example.

D3.4HW Describing data
1 a Range = 22, Mean = 42.0625, Median = 43, Mode = 42
 b 24, it is much lower than the other values
 c Range = 5, Mean = 43.267, Median = 43, Mode = 42
 d The range was high originally, because of the extreme value. This value also dragged the mean down. The median and mode were unaffected. The data set with 24 removed is more reliable.
2 a 995.3 ml
 b They are correct to the nearest 10 ml, but you are more likely to get less than a litre than more.
 c 17 ml
 d 1.7%
 The machines are fairly accurate, but tend to fill a little short. This comes to a large difference when multiplied by many bottles.

D3 SAT Level 6
a Cannot tell (you don't know how many lengths each pupil swam)
b 10.375 lengths

EXTENSION

D4 Probability experiments

D4.1HW Theoretical probability

1 a $\frac{2}{5}$ **b** $\frac{1}{25}$ **c** $\frac{1}{5}$

2 a $\frac{1}{12}$ **b** $\frac{1}{6}$ **c** $\frac{1}{2}$

3 a $\frac{1}{18}$ **b** $\frac{1}{6}$ **c** $\frac{1}{3}$ not counting 0   **d** $\frac{4}{9}$

D4.2HW Experimental probability

It will, on average, take $\frac{10}{4}$ goes to get any one of the digits.

It will then, on average, take $\frac{10}{3}$ goes to get any of the three remaining digits.

It will then, on average, take $\frac{10}{2}$ goes to get either of the two remaining digits.

It will then, on average, take 10 goes to get the last digit.

$\frac{10}{4} + \frac{10}{3} + + \frac{10}{2} + 10 = 20\frac{2}{3}$

So, it is likely to take 21 goes to get all four digits.

D4.3HW Experiment versus theory

a $\frac{1}{8}$
b $\frac{3}{8}$
c $\frac{3}{8}$
d $\frac{1}{8}$

For 100 goes:

Amount of money in $= 200p$

Amount of money won $= 2 \times 20p \times 100 \times \frac{1}{8} = 500p$

So the player of the game is likely to be better off.

D4 SAT Level 5

a $\frac{1}{2}$ **b** HT, TH , TT
c $\frac{1}{4}$ **d** $\frac{1}{2}$

D4 SAT Level 6

a Shana, because she threw the dice more times
b Biased, because red and blue are more frequent than green and yellow
c $\frac{186}{520} = 0.358$ (to 3 d.p.)
d $\frac{75}{320} = 0.144$ (to 3 d.p.)

A5 Equations and graphs

A5.1HW Solving linear equations

1 a 18   **b** 15
  c 5   **d** 31
  e 2   **f** 35
  g 23   **h** 13.3
  i 16   **j** 6

2 a 24   **b** 320
  c 5   **d** 28
  e 5   **f** $\frac{-3}{7}$

A5.2HW Using formulae

1 $k = w - px, x = \dfrac{(w - k)}{p}$

2 $x = \dfrac{(bd - bc)}{a}, a = \dfrac{(bd - bc)}{x}, c = d - \dfrac{ax}{b}$

3 $w = \dfrac{(ck - p)}{x^2}, p = ck - wx^2, x = \dfrac{\sqrt{(ck - p)}}{x}$ or $x = \dfrac{b(d - c)}{a}$,

$a = \dfrac{b(d - c)}{x}$

A5.3HW Brackets and negatives

1 257
2 25
3 36
4 26
5 77
6 70

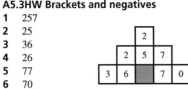

A5.4HW Generating sequences

1 a D   **b** C
  c A   **d** B

2 a 6, 11, 16, 21, 26   **b** 3, 10, 17, 24, 31
  c 0, 3, 8, 15, 24   **d** 2, 8, 18, 32, 50
  e $\frac{1}{3}, \frac{1}{6}, \frac{1}{9}, \frac{1}{12}, \frac{1}{15}$ **f** $\frac{3}{4}, \frac{4}{5}, \frac{5}{6}, \frac{6}{7}, \frac{7}{8}$

3 a Linear, $T(n) = 11n + 1$
  b Linear, $T(n) = 6n - 5$
  c Linear, $T(n) = 10 - 2n$
  d Quadratic, $T(n) = n^2 + 10$

EXTENSION

A5.5HW Spot the sequence

1 **a** 2, 5, 10, 17; $T(n) = n^2 + 1$.
Each pattern is a square plus one tile.

b 2, 8, 18, 32; $T(n) = 2n^2$.
Each pattern is two squares, each n by n

2 **a** 0, 2, 6, 12, 20

b $K = F(F - 1)$

c Each person kisses everyone but themselves, so $(F - 1)$ kisses. Everyone in total makes $F(F - 1)$ kisses.

3 **a** Inner square $n \times n$. Outer square $(n + 2) \times (n + 2)$
Number of tiles = outer square − inner square
$$= (n + 2)^2 - n^2$$

b Square n by n, plus extra strip of length n and width 2. Answer is $n^2 + 2n$.

A5.6HW Solving problems

Task 1
$T(n) = 4n - 30$
Student's own work

Task 2
In an $n \times n$ jigsaw there are 4 Cs, $(n - 2)^2$ Ms and $4(n - 2)$ Es.
In an $m \times n$ jigsaw there are 4 Cs, $(n - 2)(m - 2)$ Ms and
$2(n - 2) + 2(m - 2) = 2(n \times m - 4)$ Es.

A5.7HW Graphs of equations

1 **a and b** Student's own answer

c The added number gives the y − intercept.

2 **a and b** Student's own answer

c The number in front of the x gives the gradient, here they are all greater than 1.

A5.8HW Real life graphs

1
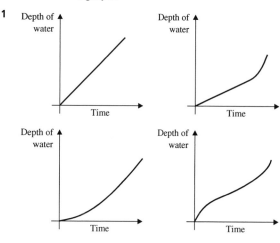

2 **a** D   **b** B
    c C   **d** E
    e A

3 **a**   **b**

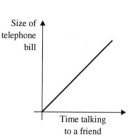

c   **d**

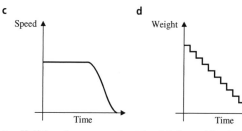

4 **a** Half the cola was poured out then left for a while, then the rest of the cola was poured out, or similar.

b The tea cooled at first, then remained at room temperature.

c The ball was dropped and bounced, each bounce wasn't so high as the previous.

A5 SAT Level 5

a 4   **b** Grey tiles   **c** 1 black, 60 grey
d 10   **e** 20

A5 SAT Level 6

a **i** 5   **ii** 7   **b** $3(3s)$
c Line passing through the points (1, 8) and (7, 50).
d $p = 7s + 1$

S5   Polygons

S5.1HW Constructing triangles
1   Angles are 33°, 58°, 89°
2   Angles are 34°, 34°, 112°
3   Angles are 31°, 100°, 49°
4   Angles are 22°, 107°, 51°
5   Angles are 41°, 55°, 84°

S5.2HW Constructing quadrilaterals
1-4 Student's own work
5   **a**   AC = 19 m (to nearest m).
     b   DB = 18
     c   Perimeter = 50 m

S5.3HW Constructing 3-D shapes
1   **a**   Net of a cube with sides 2 cm
     b   Net of a tetrahedron with sides 4 cm
     c   Net of a triangular prism
     d   Net of a cuboid
2   **a**   Cone
     b   Cylinder
     c   Cube
     d   Cuboid
     e   Sphere
     f   Square based pyramid
     g   Pentagonal prism
     h   Truncated cone
     c, d and **g** are prisms

S5.4HW Constructing perpendicuars
1   **a, b** Student's own work
     c   **i**   AC = 3.1 cm
              ii   XZ = 1.8 cm
2   Student's own work

S5.5HW Properties of polygons
There are no unique solutions to this investigation.

S5.6HW Tessellating polygons
There are no unique solutions to this investigation.

S5 SAT Level 5

a   **b**   **c**

S5 SAT Level 6

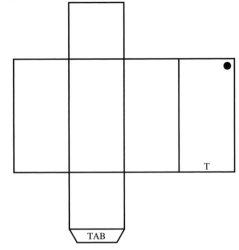

EXTENSION